MAPPING
THE
WORLD

MAPPING THE WORLD

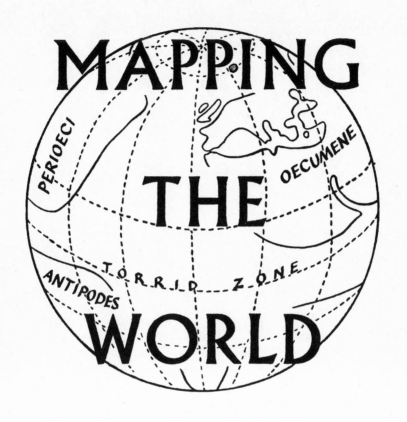

ERWIN RAISZ

ABELARD-SCHUMAN, NEW YORK

Printed in the United States of America
Published simultaneously in Canada
by Nelson, Foster & Scott, Ltd.

CONTENTS

LIST OF ILLUSTRATIONS

List of Illustrations

ACKNOWLEDGMENTS

The author owes much to the courtesy of the McGraw-Hill Book Company for permitting the use of many illustrations from his *General Cartography*. Mrs. Donald Smith helped with typing and setting right a good number of grammatical errors. Robert W. Knox, assistant director of the U.S. Coast and Geodetic Survey, read and corrected the chapters on triangulation and on charting. But chief credit is due to the editor of Abelard-Schuman for straightening out the author's tangled manuscript.

ERWIN RAISZ

TO THE READER

Dear Reader:

Did you ever wonder, looking at a map or whirling a globe, how the intricate shape of continents, shorelines, rivers and mountains came to be mapped, and who designed the system of parallels and meridians? Or how people found out, in the first place, that the earth is shaped like a globe? If we had not been told so I am not at all sure that you or I would have found it out ourselves.

The mapping of the earth is a fascinating story. It took a long time —thousands of years. The history of maps is older than history itself, if we date history from the time of written records. All hunting and herding people could draw maps of their own region long before they could read or write. The earliest maps of larger parts of the world may have been made in India or China, but only a very few maps from Babylon survived. The science of map-making really started with the ancient Greeks after they discovered the spherical shape of the earth.

Leadership in map-making shows a peculiar shift. Greece, Italy, Spain, Portugal, the Netherlands, France, England, Germany, and Switzerland all had their day, and now it may be our turn. Our present maps do not do justice to the rich carpet of the earth which we can see from an airplane. Airplane photography gives us a wonderful chance to do something new. Perhaps some of you reading this story will be inspired to take up the profession of cartography and will produce a new kind of map—the real portrait of Mother Earth.

Sincerely yours,

ERWIN RAISZ

13

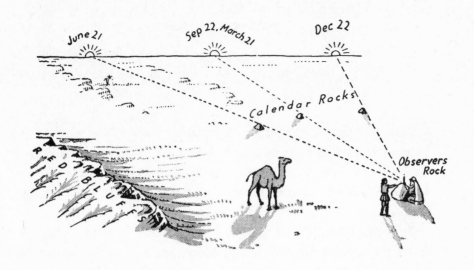

1

THE FIRST MAP

Calendar Rocks. It all started when Beshan of the Red Bluffs in Libya expected company and could not go to the Trading Bay on the Sea. Every winter, when the sun rode lower in the sky than on any other day, the dwellers of the desert started on their journey. They knew that the sun rises and sets farthest toward the north at a date which we now call June 21, and the farthest toward the south on December 21. They called these days by other names then. Years ago, Beshan's father had placed rocks to mark the spot where the sun set farthest to the south of west in summer and farthest to the north of west in winter, and one rock also where the sun set midway in spring and fall, to mark the exact east–west line. These they called the Calendar Rocks. Rarely did anyone pass by; so they had to make their own calendar.

Beshan looked at his son, Ahab, a stalwart youth of fifteen, and after talking it over with his wife decided to let Ahab lead the caravan, since Beshan couldn't go this time. Ahab was eager to go, as he had never

15

been to the sea. As water could be found only at a few specific places, it was most important that Ahab should not lose his way, for without drinking water the people of the caravan might perish.

Beshan's Map. Beshan started to explain to his son how to get to the Trading Bay. As he spoke he drew lines in the sand with a stick and used flat rocks, piled sand, and gravel to make his directions clearer. He put a piece of black charcoal on the ground to mark his tent under the Red Bluffs.

On the first day, Beshan told his son, he should start somewhat left of the rising sun. The sun would soon shift toward the south but Ahab should note the notch in the distance, through which the rising sun shines, and keep his direction until he reached it, when the sun would set behind him. There he would find water and spend the first night.

The second morning Ahab was to climb on top of a hill, from which he would see the Shining Mountains of white rock in the distance. Far to the left of the rising sun he would see a gap shaped like a V. Then Beshan piled stones upon each other and buried them half way with sand like the fan-shaped slopes coming from the knobs (rounded mountains, see Figure 1). At the Shining Mountains would be the second camp.

The third day would be the most difficult because of a large basin of soft quicksand, dreaded by camels and men. Ahab was told to turn half left from the rising sun toward Pilot Knob, a cone-shaped hill not far from the Shining Mountains. Pilot Knob and the gap should always be kept in a line, and Ahab would frequently have to look backward as he traveled to maintain this direction. In the afternoon he would reach Quicksand Basin. By skirting it to the north he would pass two palms and the converging tracks of other travelers. Along those tracks would be the only place where the soft sand could be crossed safely.

The fourth day, following the tracks straight to the north, would bring Ahab and his caravan to the Great Salt Water. He was to come

16

Fig. 1. Beshan's map

out at Trading Bay, a long beach with one big headland on the left and a double headland on the right.

By this time Beshan had built a perfect relief model of the land, with the flat rocks, sand, gravel, and stones. Every feature was in true proportion and was in the right direction from every other. It was not as Beshan had ever seen the land, for he looked at it from the height of his eyes, but it was made as the birds see it from above. Yet it was clear and understandable.

Ahab's copy. But how could Ahab remember all these details? Any mistake might mean trouble. Then he had a bright idea. He took a piece of charcoal and drew the whole thing on a tight waterskin mounted on a camel. The goat skin was small, so he had to draw everything smaller but *proportionately* at the correct *scale*.

Thanks to his map, Ahab reached the Trading Bay as planned. The sea fascinated him, and when he saw the purple sail of a ship he was elated. The captain of the ship was enormously interested in the map on

17

the goatskin. He took pen and ink and made a copy of it to add to a large chart of his own. The captain's copy of Ahab's map was still smaller in scale but also in correct proportions and with the right directions. Then they traded the skins, dried meat, dates, and herbs of

Fig. 2. Ahab draws map on waterbag

the desert, for knives, purple cloth, and ornaments made in a distant city. The captain was so pleased by the boy's intelligence that he gave a present to Ahab and asked him to join him the following year. The captain's name was Marinus of Tyre and the year was 100 A.D. We will meet him again.

Mapping is born with us. Beshan, of course, was only one of many hunters, shepherds, soldiers, and others who made maps over thousands of years to show how to get from one place to another. Some were drawn with a stick in the sand; some, like those of the Eskimo, were pieces of charred wood sewn to a sealskin, thus making a permanent record. But all of them laid out the map *as seen from above*, although the map makers never saw the land that way. They put down what they knew and not what they saw. The scale of these primitive maps was almost correct, but often one day's journey was shown as the same

18

Fig. 3. Marinus of Tyre meets Ahab at Trading Bay

length as another's, even though not so much ground was covered because of rough going.

Apparently making maps to scale and as seen from above is something born with men—but much better developed by hunters and herders, by people moving around a great deal, than by city dwellers.

Be oriented. Try to draw a map yourself after a trip. Don't worry because it doesn't look like the map of a professional map maker. If it shows the way you went and what you saw, it will be a precious record of your trip. And it will teach you to observe better and make a better map on the next trip. It will teach you also something very important to remember all your life: to be oriented. That is to know always, even without thinking of it, which way is north, south, east, or west. All the hunting and herding people know this, and after some practice we can also. It is easy when the sun is up or if you can see the polar star. Every Scout Manual will tell you how to use a compass, wind direction, a mossy tree, etc. But the best help is always to watch your landmarks and lay them out on a map either in your mind or on paper.

2

THE EARTH'S PORTRAIT TAKES SHAPE

Even before the time of Marinus of Tyre people speculated about the size and shape of the earth, and left records of their ideas.

What would you think of the nature of this world if you had never read a geography book? You probably would never get the idea that the earth is spherical, like a huge ball, as you do not see it that way. You may go up on a high mountain and look around the great circuit of the horizon. It may look flat, perhaps hilly, but it does not give the impression that you are on a sphere.

The disk-like earth. No wonder people first thought the earth was a flat disk. They knew that if one went far enough in any direction, one was likely to hit the sea. So they made their disk float in the ocean. But earth is heavier than water, and the earth would not float unless hollow inside, like a buoy. Thus they thought that there was a huge cavern inside and that the spirits of their ancestors dwelt there.

Above the disk was sketched a rotating cover called the firmament, holding the sun, moon, and the planets. The stars were little holes in the firmament through which shone the glory of heaven above. What held the whole system together and what was beyond the waters they did not know. But do we know now what is beyond the stars and galaxies?

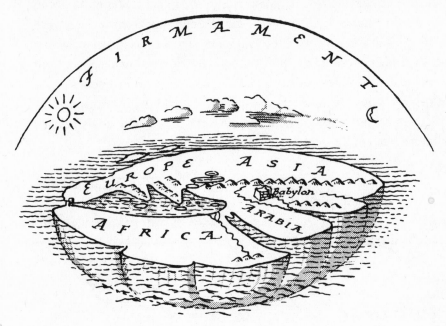

Fig. 4. The Babylonians thought that the earth was a hollow disk

Latitude and longitude. This was a beautiful system and was taught in the schools of Babylon and Greece for a long time, but there were some disturbing facts. First of all, as they began to trade with India and sailed boldly through the Pillars of Hercules (Gibraltar), they found that they could go a great deal farther west and east than they could go north and south. So some geographers made the earth oblong instead of disk-shaped. If we speak of latitude and longitude we are following this idea.

Parallels and meridians. Then someone came up with the idea of putting on the map east–west and north–south halfway lines which crossed at the Island of Rhodes, the supposed center of the world. Now they had two reference lines, and each point on the earth could be located by saying that it was so many stadia (ten stadia make about one nautical mile) north or south the latitude way from Rhodes, and so many stadia east or west the longitude way. Eratosthenes, of whom we shall hear more later, went beyond this, and around 250 B.C. put seven east–west lines, called parallels, and seven north–south lines, called meridians, on his map—not equally spaced but going through the most important cities of that age, so that they could now measure distance from more than one place.

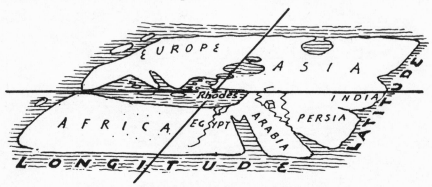

Fig. 5. The idea of latitude and longitude came from the Greeks in the fourth century B.C.

The earth as a sphere. There was trouble, however, with this elongated flat world. The Greeks were good astronomers. They noted that at every eclipse of the moon the earth's shadow was a circular arc of the same shape. If the eclipse came near sunset, and the earth's surface were flat, its shadow on the moon would look straight.

How, also, could one explain on a flat earth the fact that one sees the top of the sails of approaching ships first, and after they depart one can still see the sails long after the hull sinks below the horizon? But what clinched the matter was that when they sailed north, let us say a hundred miles every day, the angle of the polar star above the horizon

22

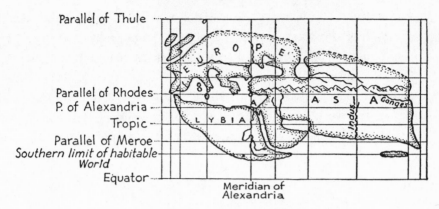

Fig. 6. The parallels and meridians of Eratosthenes.
(*From Raisz:* General Cartography)

got higher and higher evenly with the same degree. No flat earth could explain this. It was hard to see it that way, yet in the fourth century B.C. the Greeks accepted the fact that they inhabited the surface of a spherical body. They were, however, greatly disturbed by the thought that people could live on the underside of it without falling off; gravitation had not yet been discovered.

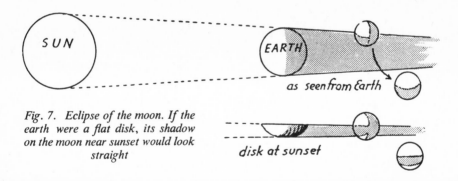

Fig. 7. Eclipse of the moon. If the earth were a flat disk, its shadow on the moon near sunset would look straight

Eratosthenes. They all agreed that the earth must be a very huge ball; otherwise it would not look so flat. But how big? One of the neatest calculations in all history was made by Eratosthenes, the Librarian of

Alexandria (270–195 B.C.). He was not a librarian as we know them. Alexandria, the main port of Egypt, was founded by Alexander the Great and was built on a sandbar with a lagoon behind it, like Atlantic City or Galveston. From here Alexander's Greek general, Ptolemaeus, and his descendants, ruled over Egypt. They made it the most cultured city in the world. The library was something like a university, with spacious colonnades, where scientists and philosophers from all over

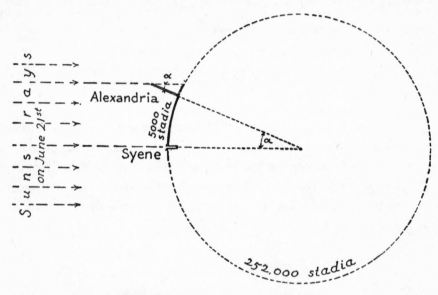

Fig. 8. Eratosthenes measures the earth.
(*From Raisz:* General Cartography)

the world taught and discussed scientific matters. The library had half a million volumes of books, rolls, and tablets, something unsurpassed until modern times.

Eratosthenes heard of a well in Syene, the present Aswan, at the First Cataract of the Nile where today the big dam regulates the flow of the river. In this well the sun's rays penetrated to the bottom for only a few days around June 21, which means that it was at or near the Tropic of

24

Cancer (Fig. 8). Assuming that Syene was directly south from Alexandria, and knowing that the distance was 5,000 stadia, all Eratosthenes had to do was measure the angle of the noonday sun in Alexandria on June 21. This he did, and found it to be one-fiftieth of a circle. If one-fiftieth of the circle is 5,000 stadia the whole circle is 250,000 stadia in circumference. There are 360° of latitude in a full circle. This makes one degree almost exactly 700 stadia. If we accept one stadia as one-tenth of a nautical mile, this was a remarkably good approximation. The actual length of the earth's girdle is 21,600 nautical miles, which is 86 per cent of 250,000 as Eratosthenes figured it.

This is all the more remarkable because Syene is a half degree north of the Tropic; the distance is only 453 miles, and Syene is 3° off the north–south line, and the angle is 7° 05′ instead of 7° 12′ as Eratosthenes measured it. But these mistakes compensated so well that the final figure was not far off.

Posidonius. So far so good. One hundred years later, however, another scientist, Posidonius, repeated this measurement with better instruments and better results. His measurement, however, was mistakenly recorded by the first-century A.D. geographer, Strabo, to be 180,000 stadia. And it was this small earth on which a degree was only 500 stadia which was accepted later by Ptolemy, and after him by the geographers of the Renaissance, in spite of the fact that the Arabs made much more exact measurements in the Middle Ages.

Sixteen hundred years after Posidonius, Columbus, figuring on this smaller earth ball, thought that by sailing west about 5,000 miles he must arrive at Asia. (Actually the distance between Spain and south-east Asia is nearer 14,000 miles.) When Columbus found certain islands 4,000 miles from Spain he could only think that he must have reached the islands of Eastern Asia. Here he found dark-skinned people, small in stature and with smooth hair. He was not far mistaken when he thought them to be the inhabitants of the Farther Indies, whom we now call Indonesians, as they were of the same race. He thought that he was in some part of India not yet known to Europeans. Our calling Indians by that name can be traced back to Strabo's record of Posidonius's measurement, underestimating the earth's size.

Thanks to the scientific turn of the Greek mind, certain earth-facts were well established at the beginning of the Christian era.

Degrees and minutes. They knew that the earth was ball-shaped and how large it was. They knew about the equator and the poles. Hyparchus, the great astronomer, proposed that the equator and the meridian circles be divided into 360°, a degree into sixty minutes, and a minute into sixty seconds. This he learned from the Babylonians who used a system of numbers based on six or twelve rather than our system based on ten. The twelve months of the year and the twice-twelve hours of the day also came from Babylon. They defined with great accuracy the tilt of the earth's axis against the path of the sun. We know now that it is really the earth's path around the sun and not the sun's path around the earth.

Strabo even tells about a globe made by Crates around 100 B.C.

Fig. 9. Crates' globe.
(*From Raisz:* General Cartography)

Crates, the chief librarian of Pergamum in Asia Minor, was familiar with the size of the known world which the Greeks called *ecumene*. He knew also the size of the earth, from Eratosthenes. When he made a big globe and tried to draw the ecumene upon it he found that it covered scarcely a quarter of the sphere. Such a lopsided earth would not agree with the Greek idea of balance and symmetry, so Crates put three more continents on it from his own imagination. This is the first anticipation of the Americas and Australia. This was the beginning of the huge *Terra Australis*, or southern continent, which appeared with various shapes on almost all maps of the world before Captain Cook sailed around Antarctica. We will see examples later.

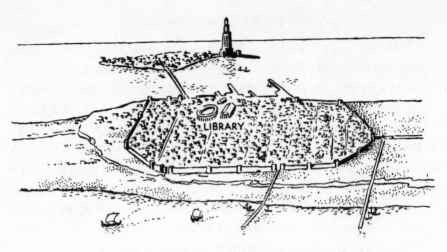

*Fig. 10. Alexandria was the center of science at the
time of Christ*

3

THE EARTH SCIENCE OF PTOLEMY

In the time of Christ the map of the lands of the earth was still terribly
crude. Travel was difficult in those days, and the sea captains kept their
knowledge to themselves. Many of them knew a great deal, but a
master mind was needed to put all the facts together.

Marinus. All we know of Marinus of Tyre is that Ptolemy based the
construction of his map on a chart of Marinus's which is either lost or
was never finished. Wherever Ptolemy differed he carefully explained
why. Thus we know that the Marinus chart was like Ptolemy's except
that it was on a square grid of parallels and meridians. How Marinus
got all his data we do not know; it could have been somewhat like the
story in the first chapter. Maybe he inherited the secret knowledge of
the great Phoenician sea traders and colonizers of the past. The important fact is that here at about 120 A.D. we had a map, or rather a

28

sea chart, of the world which may look very crude to us, but considering that it was made without even a compass, it is one of the greatest monuments of human culture.

Ptolemy. Most of our knowledge of the Earth and Heaven, as the ancients knew it, comes from a great scientist and a very prolific writer, Claudius Ptolemy from Alexandria. His name suggests that he may have descended from the house of the Ptolemies, which ruled Egypt and Palestine from the time of Alexander the Great until Cleopatra was bitten by the asp in 31 B.C. and the Romans took over. Claudius, however, wrote his books much later, sometime about 120–150 A.D.

He rejected the idea of some scientists that the earth revolved around the sun, because that "would cause a wind that would sweep everything off the earth." He believed that the universe was filled with air. He thought that the earth was the center of the universe, and the sun, moon, and stars moved around it. He drew very complex looped lines called *epicycles* to explain the motion of the planets. So great was his authority that even in the sixteenth century most people still believed in his ideas.

For us his most important contribution is his seven-volume geography book, particularly the atlas which went with it. The atlas contained one world map and twenty-six detailed maps, the first known atlas in history.

The earliest known copy of the atlas dates from the thirteenth century and some people think that the map, as shown in Figure 12, is thirteenth-century Byzantine work. The original Ptolemy map may have been cruder, but whenever it was drawn it embodied the knowledge of the ancients.

Projections. First of all, here we have a *map projection*. We cannot flatten the surface of a ball but we can draw parallels and meridians on it and draw somewhat similar parallels and meridians on flat paper and

29

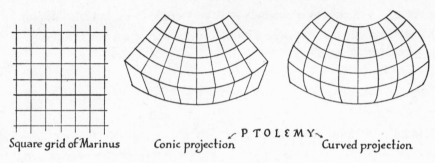

Square grid of Marinus   Conic projection   Curved projection

Fig. 11. Ptolemy's projections

relate a map to them. Ptolemy's map is drawn on either of two such systems, both of them much better than the square grid of Marinus, on which the meridians do not bunch together at the poles (Figure 11). Obviously Ptolemy's designs have less distortion. His map does not show the whole world, only the ecumene, and for this it is a very good projection.

Ptolemy's errors. It is unfair, perhaps, to start with Ptolemy's mistakes, but they are the most revealing. The most striking is the very elongated Mediterranean Sea. One would think an Alexandrian would have known better. Ptolemy had a fairly good idea of how long this sea was, but he worked with the smaller earth-ball of Strabo (see Chapter 2) on which a degree was also smaller, only 500 stadia instead of 700. He had to spread the 3,000 miles of the Mediterranean Sea over 62° of longitude; actually it is only 42°. This made the sea very drawn out lengthwise, east to west, a feature which prevailed on maps for 1,500 years.

He also pulled southern Africa and eastern Asia together and made the Indian Ocean an enclosed basin. This was his own idea and the reasons for it are not quite clear, particularly as it was known that Hanno circumnavigated Africa around 600 B.C. Ptolemy also shows a huge river flowing west all along the middle of the Sahara Desert.

30

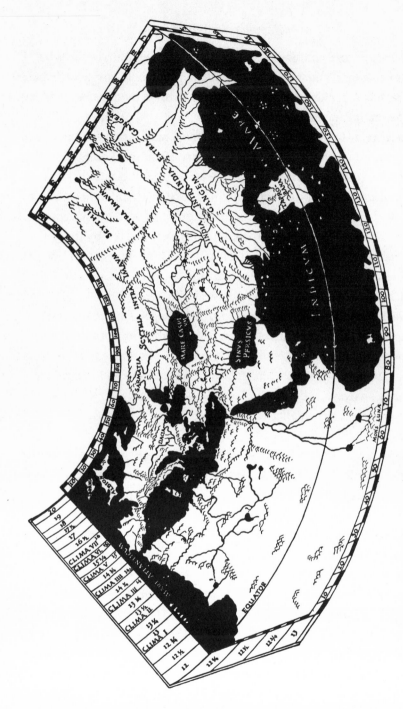

Fig. 12. Ptolemy's map. This is a simplified drawing made after the fifteenth-century copies of Ptolemy's world map. (From Raisz: General Cartography)

Here he may have confused the Niger and the Senegal rivers. What a pity that this marvellous river does not exist! It would surpass the Nile in giving life to the desert. This river was still shown on maps of Africa until the end of the eighteenth century.

Scandinavia is a small island on Ptolemy's map, and near by, at the northern limit of the map, is the legendary island of Thule. This was described as the land where the elements of the ancients (air, water, earth, and fire) are not distinct, as in the Mediterranean, but merge into each other. This may be a poetic description of icy, misty, volcanic Iceland. The Aral Sea is combined with the Caspian, fed by the Volga, the Oxus, and Yaxartes rivers. This is interesting because in ancient times these rivers actually emptied into the Caspian Sea.

It is rather odd that Ptolemy missed the Deccan Peninsula, and combined Ceylon and Sumatra into the huge Taprobana Island, although detailed sailing directions were available for both.

Perhaps the most portentous of Ptolemy's mistakes was making Eurasia 180° instead of 130° long, from Portugal to China. This made Columbus's voyage even more plausible, as he figured that China was even nearer than the smaller earth-ball of Strabo indicated.

Roman maps. Ptolemy marks the peak of the geography of the ancients. The Romans did not add much. They were practical people and did not care about the problems raised by the parallels and meridians and the length of a degree. All they wanted was a practical map with which to get around and to use in war and in administering the provinces. They returned to the disk-shaped map of the early Greeks because it was simpler, and they called it the *Orbis Terrarum*, the circuit of the world. It was this map which was followed in the Middle Ages and which dominated geographical thinking for over a thousand years. Note that most of the orb is Roman Empire. Russia (Sarmatia), Siberia (Scythia), China (Seres), Persia, Arabia, and mid-Africa (Ethiopia) are just outlying provinces.

32

Fig. 13. The Roman map: a reconstruction from medieval copies. (From Raisz: General Cartography)

33

At about the same time the Chinese made a map in which China is the "Middle Kingdom" (Ching-hwa) and the rest of the world consists of islands around it. What would have happened if a Roman and a Chinese cartographer had met!

Fig. 14. Early Chinese map

4

THE MIDDLE AGES AND THE
PORTOLAN CHARTS

 HIS monk of the Middle Ages is drawing a map of the world. He has only a few books of ancient church fathers to help him. He rarely goes outside of the monastery, and even then his eyes are not cast down upon the earth but are lifted up to the shining heavens. He does not travel, as Marinus did, to collect information from everywhere. His soul is turned inward. When he draws a map he does not try to make the world as it is but as it should be according to the God-inspired image in his mind. The

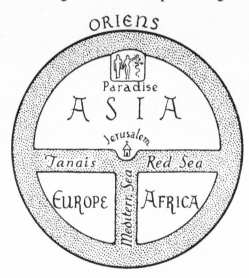

Fig. 15. The perfection and symmetry of the T-in-O (Orbis Terrarum) *maps had great appeal for the medieval minds.* (*From Raisz:* General Cartography)

irregular outlines of Ptolemy's map do not appeal to him. He prefers the round Roman map, but even this is too irregular for his craving for divine perfection. But maybe it can be improved here and there! The Mediterranean may be straightened a little. The Roman map shows the Aegean Sea, the Marmara Sea, the Black Sea, the Sea of Azov, and the Don River, like beads on a string. These could be combined into a single arm of the sea. The Nile and the Red Sea may make an opposite arm. He wants to have Jerusalem in the center. Did not the Bible say: "I have set her in the midst of nations and countries are round about her. . . ."? Now let us see what the monk gets. He looks at the map with pleasure and surprise. It shows a letter O and in it a letter T—*Orbis Terrarum!* Not only did God create the world in perfect symmetry but he even shaped it according to its Latin initials. God be praised! This perfect arrangement appealed enormously to the medieval mind and we find hundreds of these T-in-O maps in medieval manuscripts.

Peculiarly, the Moslem people made a round diagrammatic map,

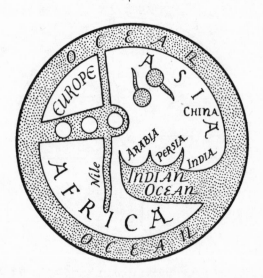

Fig. 16. A medieval diagrammatic Arab world map. Translated and simplified. (From Raisz: General Cartography)

36

too, at about the same time. It was used in school geography books as early as the tenth century. The Arab round map was far less beautifully symmetrical, but much more true.

Compass. For the seaman of the Middle Ages the T-in-O maps had much less appeal because he could not use them for navigation. For him even the Roman or the Ptolemy maps were too crude, particularly since he now had a new tool with which to find directions. Some people had brought a black stone from the East which had a miraculous quality: if you rubbed it on a needle and free-floated this needle in a cup of water the needle always turned north–south, no matter which way the cup was turned. The needle could even be hung on a string or balanced on a pivot, but in this case the south side had to be weighted slightly; otherwise it would point upward.

The medieval seamen were excellent in dead reckoning. This means that they knew fairly well how many miles they sailed or rowed, and they could estimate distances with great accuracy. Direction, however, was another matter. Overcast skies and variable winds could easily turn them about. But now they had a *compass* to direct their course. *Any place can be located in relation to any other place by distance and direction.* Now both could be determined and the time was ripe for a real sea chart.

Portolan charts. We do not know who made it, but around 1300 A.D. there appeared a chart of the Mediterranean and Black Seas which was almost miraculous. Nothing so accurate had ever appeared before and it was so good that it was copied again and again and was used for actual navigation for over 300 years.

Volumes have been written about the origin of this chart. One thing is certain—it was the result of a systematic compass survey, as indicated by the radiating lines or compass roses on the chart. Where no survey was made, as around the Atlantic Ocean and Baltic Sea, it was just as crude as the other maps of the time. Most likely it was made by the navigators of the Genoese Admiralty around 1280, because the first charts appeared around Genoa; also the Black Sea, which was a Genoese trading area, is so well shown.

Fig. 18. Medieval world maps show the Mediterranean area accurately, but the rest of the map is very crudely drawn

It was decidedly a sea chart; the land is handled in a rough, sometimes decorative way, while the coast is overloaded with letters. Names are placed so that they can be read from the nearest side if you place the chart on a table on shipboard. The chart is criss-crossed by "rhumb" lines, showing compass directions, usually radiating from 16 or 32 centers. The principal directions are always black, the halves green, the quarters red. In no copy would it be otherwise. These rhumb lines are

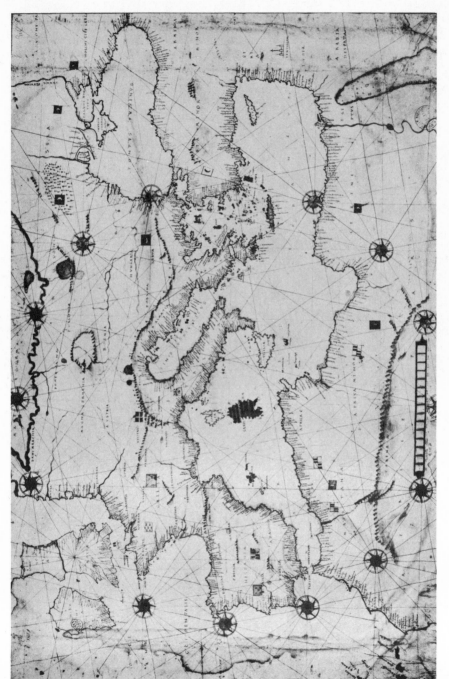

Fig. 17. The medieval portolan charts were surprisingly accurate and very beautiful. (From: Imago Mundi)

not only for decoration. The parallel ruler (see Figure 49) had not yet been invented, but the navigator, knowing his position, could always find some rhumb lines near by to show what to expect in each compass direction.

These charts were copied all around the western Mediterranean, in Venice, Genoa, Palermo, and in the Balearic Islands. Sometimes a hundred copyists were engaged to draw them on parchment. They appear even in Arabic, but the usual language is Latin.

Later these charts were made· more elaborate. Often they were included in little atlases, showing also a world map (Figure 18) of the crudest type but with an excellently drawn Mediterranean. Harbor charts, tables of the altitude of the sun, were often added, as well as calendars, and even medical advice—something like a sea almanac. With the great cathedrals the portolan charts rank as the fairest of the products of the Middle Ages.

5

MAP MAKERS· MEET THE NEW WORLD

Arabian maps. By the late Middle Ages the attitude of the people had changed. They no longer sought for revelations from the heavens alone; they began to find this earth very fascinating too. The Crusaders and their followers marveled at the buildings and the splendor of the Mohammedan peoples. They learned about the books and maps of the great Moslem geographers. They saw the large map by Edrisi, the Arabian prince in exile, drawn in 1154 (Figure 19), at the court of King Roger II, the Norman ruler of Sicily. Nothing like this had been made since Ptolemy. They found that the Arabian children were taught geography and had school atlases at a time when most people in Europe could not read or write.

Eastern contacts. In the fourteenth century people read the story of Marco Polo, who became the ambassador of the Great Khan of China. They learned of a great civilization, in many ways higher than their own. They saw also the ruins of the Roman Empire and of Greece, and when they passed through Italy and Constantinople they found copies of Ptolemy's works. The books of Ptolemy were studied, and translated into Latin, and in the next century over a hundred editions were published.

With the fall of the Byzantine Empire in 1453 a number of Greek scientists came west. They brought with them the wisdom of the ancient Greeks. The world was ready for the Great Revival—the Renaissance.

Printing and engraving. A German bookseller in Augsburg had the idea of carving letters in wood in reverse. He set these letters up in a frame, inked them, and pressed them against paper. He could easily print in a day hundreds of sheets which would have taken many months

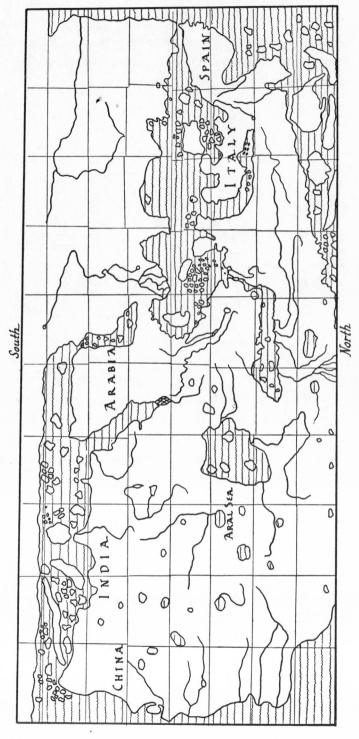

Fig. 19. Outline of Edrisi's map of 1154

to copy by hand. This meant that not only princes but also more modest citizens could afford books. Maps and pictures could similarly be carved into wood and printed.

Fig. 20. Map maker and printer of the sixteenth century

By the end of the century even a better way was found to engrave maps. A very smooth copper plate was lightly waxed; upon it the map was drawn in reverse, as if seen through a mirror. Then the lines and letters of the map were engraved into the copper. The entire copper plate was inked, and then the surface was rubbed clean so that the ink remained only in the grooves. The plate was pressed against damp rag paper, which took the ink out of the grooves. Extremely fine and artistic maps could be produced by this method. Until the 1820s almost all maps were engraved in copper.

Size of the earth. It is a popular belief that the people of the late Middle Ages thought the world was flat and that the bold voyage of Columbus proved it to be spherical. Actually, with the knowledge of the books of Ptolemy, Strabo, Pliny, and others, no scientist doubted that the earth was ball-shaped. But they thought it was smaller. The

Arabs and the Portuguese, however, had a better idea of the size of the earth. They believed one would have to sail over 10,000 miles from Lisbon to reach China. That is why the king's council of scientists, the "Junta de Matematicos" in Lisbon, refused to aid Columbus. They were right—with his provisions Columbus could not have reached China. It was sheer luck that, less than half way, he landed on a new continent. Columbus did not know that—he thought he was in Asia.

Discovery of America. When the news reached Europe there was great excitement among the map makers. They did not know whether the New World was a part of Asia, or something entirely separate. Here are four maps, made after Columbus's voyages, which show the confusion.

La Cosa was a seaman on Columbus's second voyage (the captain of the *Santa Maria* of the first voyage was another La Cosa). He drew his map upon his return and it is dated 1500. This is the first map to show the new world (Figure 21*a*). La Cosa did not commit himself on the Asia question, as he cut his map short on both ends.

Contarini shows North America as a part of Asia, but South America as a new continent—"Land of the Holy Cross" (Figure 21*b*).

Waldseemüller separates North America and South America, and marks their west coasts "Terra Incognita"—Unknown Land (Figure 21*c*). Why Waldseemüller put in a strait, when Columbus could not find one, is hard to explain. Perhaps Waldseemüller was cautious; it might turn out that North America was after all a part of Asia. In that case it was better to leave a strait for Marco Polo's return trip; he had sailed through the Strait of Singapore. Waldseemüller made a small map at the top of his large one, in which he did not show that strait. It is fascinating to speculate how different history would have been if this natural Panama Canal had actually been there. Spanish ships would have sailed to Oregon, California, Alaska, Japan, and China. Probably a United States from coast to coast would never have emerged.

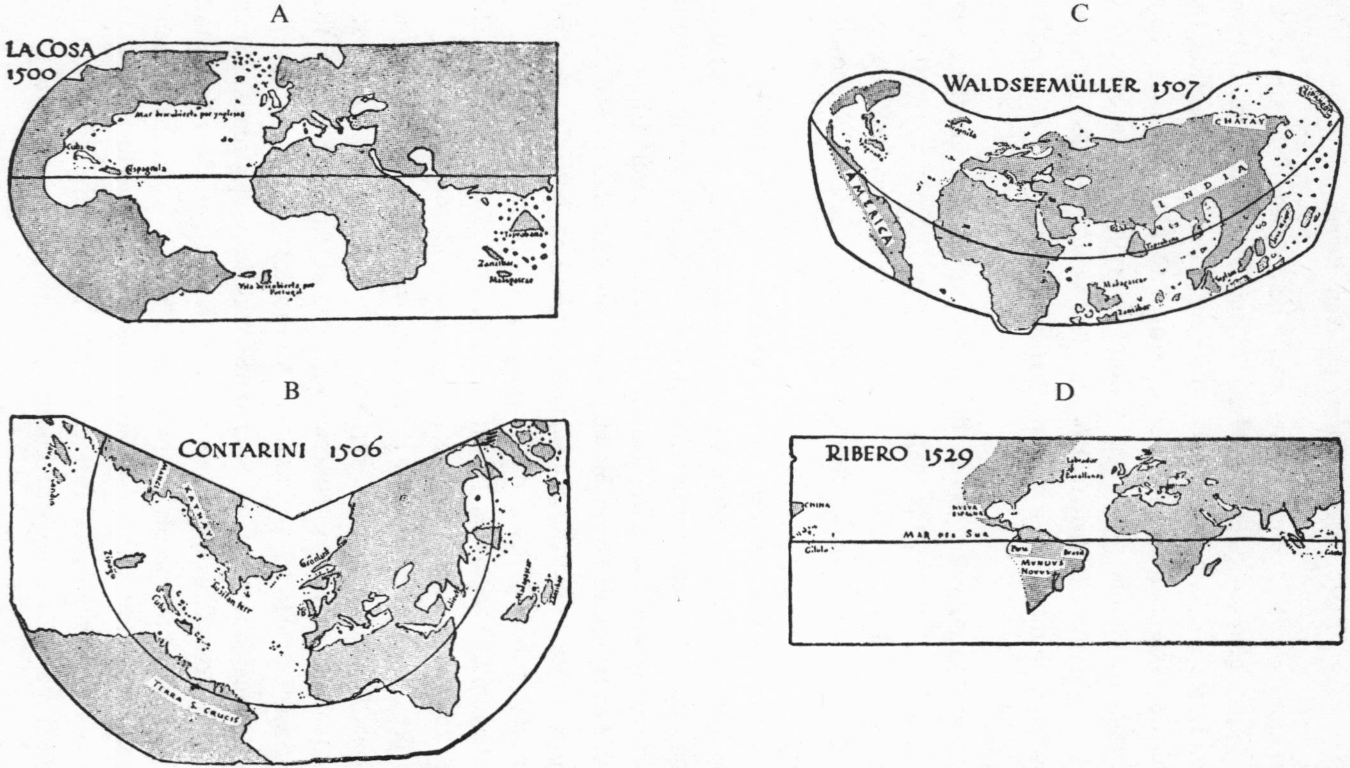

Fig. 21. *The outlines of these four famous maps show how confused map makers were by the discovery of America. (From Raisz: General Cartography)*

Waldseemüller, or Hylacomylus, the classicized name by which he was called according to the habit of Renaissance scientists, was a priest-professor and later the head of the distinguished school of St. Dié in the Vosges Mountains in northeastern France. A colleague of his was translating the records of Amerigo Vespucci, who took part in the Hojeda expedition along the Venezuela–Guiana coast in 1500 and who gave himself generous credit for his accomplishments. Waldseemüller was so impressed by Amerigo Vespucci that he wrote in the pamphlet which went with the map: "I do not see why anyone may object to naming it Amerige—that is Amerigo's Land—from Americus, the discoverer, a man of sagacious mind . . . or America, as both Europa and Asia derived their names from women," and he put the name "America" on his map of 1507. Later he found out his mistake, and the name America does not appear on his 1516 map. But others picked it up and it became so popular that nothing could be done about changing it.

The 1507 map is a remarkable work. It was printed from wood-blocks in sections and when assembled it was over 5 × 7 feet in size. It shows the world according to Ptolemy, with many additions. So great was the influence of this ancient Alexandrian that Waldseemüller discarded the marvellously correct portolan outlines of the Mediterranean and Black seas and returned to the very poor design of Ptolemy's. Waldseemüller, however, did not make the Indian Ocean an enclosed basin, but pulled China down into a second peninsula in the east. More than a thousand copies of this map were printed, but maps perish easily: they are not like books—they are taken on trips, used on shipboard and are not easily stored. So this famous map was lost until a single copy was discovered in the Castle of Prince Waldburg of Wolfegg in Würtemberg. The map is for sale. It is only fitting and proper that this map—the godfather of our continent—should come to America. But the price is high, about $200,000. Yet if every person in New York City alone gave a few cents this wonderful work could be brought here.

Diego Ribero. In 1523 a seaworn ship arrived in Sevilla with nineteen hungry and bedraggled seamen aboard. This was what remained of Admiral Magellan's proud fleet which had sailed off west three years previously to round the earth. The sailors had a marvellous story to tell. They had found the Southwest Passage, a barren, rock-bound, wind-swept strait with dangerous currents. They had sailed for months over the vastest of oceans without seeing land. They starved, ate leather, and drank foul water, until they arrived at a luscious group of islands, the Philippines, where Magellan was killed in a skirmish. They left two of their ships, and led by the Basque captain El Cano, they made their way around Africa to Spain.

The result of this voyage is shown on Diego Ribero's map of 1529 (Figure 21*d*). It looks almost like a modern map, as it shows the vast expanse of the Pacific Ocean. Europe, Asia, and Africa look smaller than on the previous maps because they had found that the earth was much larger than had been thought before. The idea of a short way to China and India was shattered.

Diego Ribero was the royal cartographer of Spain, keeper of the Padron Real (the secret royal map) for which every Spanish sea captain was supposed to report his discoveries, and which was jealously kept from other nations. Later Ribero went to Rome and drew his map from memory. The portrait of Mother Earth began to look like her—showing both faces.

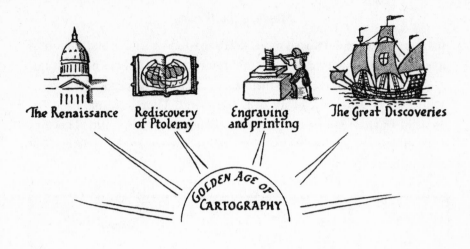

The Renaissance   Rediscovery of Ptolemy   Engraving and printing   The Great Discoveries

GOLDEN AGE OF CARTOGRAPHY

6

THE GOLDEN AGE OF CARTOGRAPHY

In the previous chapter we traced the changes in the map of the world in the sixteenth century. We saw how the Great Revival, called the Renaissance, the re-discovery of Ptolemy, the invention of printing, and the great discoveries came about almost at the same time. The result was such an outburst of map-making productivity as the world had not seen before and rarely since.

Golden Age of Dutch cartography. The first maps were mostly Italian or Spanish, as we have seen in the previous chapter; in the second half of the sixteenth century, however, the leaders in the map-making art were the Flemish and Dutch. How did this come about? Part of the answer is shown on the map (Figure 22). The "Low Countries" are located centrally in the middle of three great nations and they were in part subject to a fourth. They could get first-hand information from the sea captains of England, France, and Spain, and they were great explorers themselves. Their scientific ideas and engraving skill came largely from Germany. This was also the age of the great Dutch painters, and

47

many artists were employed in the drafting rooms of Bleau and Janszoon and other great map-making establishments. Add to this the natural Dutch industriousness and their excellent sense for good business. Dutch maps were bought all over the world. They were published in French, English, German, Spanish, Italian, and also in Latin. They are still on sale. A good copy of an Ortelius Atlas may easily fetch well over a thousand dollars.

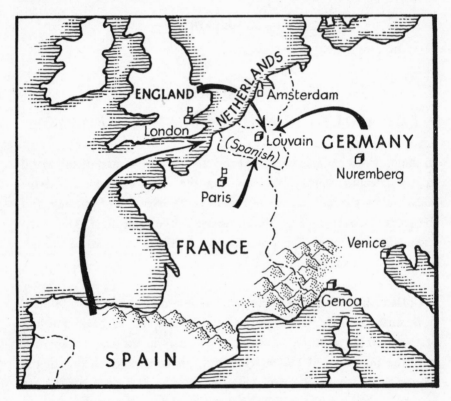

Fig. 22. The Netherlands were excellently located to become the leading map producers

Mercator. The distinguished gentleman on the left side of Figure 23 is Gerardus Mercator (1512–1594), the "father of Dutch cartography."

Fig. 23. Mercator and Hondius

He latinized his name, in accordance with the custom of that age, from Gerhart Krämer. He came from Germany, studied and settled in Louvain, Belgium. By the middle of the century he was the most honored map maker in Europe.

It sometimes happens that a map maker is too careless or is misinformed, and puts something on a map which does not belong. Others may copy him, and soon a feature is copied so often that people believe it to be true. We have already mentioned how the mistakes of Ptolemy, like the too-long Mediterranean, the great Saharan river, the island of Thule, and all his other errors, were copied and copied even 1,500 years later. Sometimes religious ideas crept in, like the four rivers coming out of Paradise, found on almost all medieval maps. Often it was pure speculation, like the *Terra Australis*, the enormous southern continent which, once introduced, was repeated on most maps.

Mercator knew his geography, and had a critical mind. He pruned out many of the popular misrepresentations. He reduced the length of the Mediterranean Sea. He made creditable maps and globes himself, and set the style for maps for centuries to come. He is best known for the Mercator projection of which we will say more in Chapter 9, but he invented other projections, too.

Mercator was followed by his son-in-law Hondius, the gentleman on the right of Figure 23, and he again by his son-in-law Jan Janszoon, and the establishment lasted over a century.

The picture reveals much of the spirit of the age. It is far too ornate for our taste, but that was the fashion then. At the top of the picture is an "armillary sphere," by which they studied latitude and longitude, the seasons, and the progress of the stars. Next is a cross staff with which they measured latitude at sea by observing the altitude of the noonday sun above the horizon. Figure 24 explains how. The higher the sun is, the closer one has to bring the crosspiece. The map in the background of Figure 23 is Mercator's famous map of Europe of 1554. Both men are gorgeously dressed and solemnly measure something on a globe. They do not look at the globe. This was just a pose, very common in old pictures, taken not only by map makers but by anybody who wanted to look scientific. We hope that they didn't try to measure distances that way. Why would that be wrong?

Fig. 24. Cross staff was used to measure the altitude of the sun or stars above the horizon

Ortelius. Figure 25 shows a map of 1580 by Ortelius, a friend of Mercator, who published the first great atlas, the *Theatrum Orbis Terrarum* in 1570. The title of the map is in an ornate "cartouche" which covers up much of the area which they knew nothing about in Ortelius's time. This practice is not entirely unknown to map makers even today. The lettering is superb. At present we imitate the early Dutch letters on our maps. The ships are not just decorations—they show the prevailing winds. See how they follow the northeast and southeast trade winds? Note the Strait of Magellan separating the

Fig. 25. America in 1580 by Ortelius; much reduced from a copper-engraved original

enormous *Terra Australis* from South America. The then newly discovered New Guinea is also added to this southern continent. South
America is fairly well mapped. The curving Amazon River records the
tragic voyage of Orellana. North America, however, was far less known.
No Mississippi River, and no Great Lakes, but the Colorado River is
extended into the legendary kingdom of Tototeac. The Saguenay River
of the Province of Quebec reaches almost to the middle of the continent.

Other Dutch map makers. It would be too much to list here all the
great Dutch map makers: the Bleau family, the Vishers, the Donckers,
and many others. The twelve-volume Bleau atlas of 1664 is perhaps the
high point of Dutch map making. Other nations imitated the style or
simply employed Dutch helpers. A few notables were: Saxton and
Speede in England, Sanson and Jailott in France, Homann and Seutter
in Germany, Olaeus Magnus in Sweden.

As we pass into the late seventeenth century there is a distinct over-
production. The maps are less beautiful; they tend to be overcrowded.
Gradually the Dutch leadership gave way to the French and the English.
The whole concept of mapping changed—art gave way to science,
imagination to accuracy. The next chapter will deal with the reformation
of cartography.

GLOBES

Behaim. In 1492—a memorable date—Martin Behaim of Nuremberg
finished his *Erdapfel* (Earth-apple), the first earth globe that survived.
He was commissioned by the Town Council to make it, which speaks
well for the cultural level of the great medieval city. Behaim was the
right man to do it. He traveled in the Azores and lived in Lisbon at
the same time as Columbus. We have no record that they met, but the
Erdapfel is the nearest representation of the geographical ideas of
Columbus when he embarked on the *Santa Maria*, to chase the sunset.
(See Figure 26.)

The globe is only twenty inches across, painted on wood, and follows Ptolemy rather closely, but shows Africa so that one can sail around it, and does not connect South Africa with India as Ptolemy did. This was seven years before Vasco da Gama actually sailed around Africa. You may still see this globe in the museum of Nuremberg, and there is also a copy of a 1493 letter from a German astronomer to the king

Fig. 26. The Behaim globe of 1492 is the first one which survived. (From Rhoem, etc., The Record of Mankind, D. C. Heath & Co.)

of Portugal, in which he describes how China could be reached by sailing west and states that the great navigator, Martin Behaim, is already in the Azores waiting for a chance and royal backing for the voyage. Of course Behaim did not know that Columbus had already returned from his first voyage. It is interesting to speculate what our history would have been if Columbus had failed, and Behaim had succeeded. Behaim settled in Lisbon, became a respected scientist, and died there in 1507.

Nuremberg became a great center for globe making. Johannes Schöner worked here. His 1515 globe shows the Strait of Magellan, five years before it was discovered. Almost every great cartographer of that age made globes, some so ornate that we do not know whether they were meant to be works of science or of art.

Coronelli. The greatest of them was Father Vincenzo Coronelli (1650–1718), a Venetian priest, one of the most prolific producers of maps, charts, and globes in history. Among others he made a thirteen-foot globe for the king of France, which revolved on an axis by clock-work. One could go inside and see the stars—tiny holes in the shell. The globe is now packed away in boxes in Versailles, but we hope it soon will be restored. Coronelli had many talents—he invented the dry dock, and his plans for draining the Venetian marshes and for the regulation of the Danube were way ahead of his time.

Fig. 27. Coronelli's globe, thirteen feet in diameter, shows the land on the outside and the stars from the inside

7

THE CASSINIS—THEY MEASURED
THE EARTH

Great-grandfather, grandfather, father, and son—the Cassinis were the greatest scientific dynasty of all time. They measured the stars, the earth, and the moon; they measured the land of France, and brilliantly performed the first great national survey. All four were in charge of the Paris Observatory, consecutively, for 122 years. The course of modern mapping was largely shaped by this family.

Jean Dominique Cassini. Perhaps the most brilliant was the founder, Jean Dominique (1625–1712), born near the French–Italian border in Perinaldo, near Nice. His first words were Italian, his last French. His Jesuit teachers in Genoa soon discovered his excellent mind and they molded it for scientific work. His success started at an early age. Even in those times it was far from usual to occupy the chair of astronomy at the University of Bologna at the age of twenty-five. Here he built a huge "scaph," a saucer, an inverted bowl of heaven with a needle in

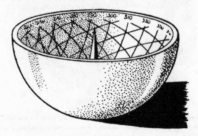

Fig. 28. A scaph—hemispherical bowl with a pin in the center

the center. Inside the bowl he traced the course of the sun, the moon, and the planets. He proved that Kepler's law of the motions of the planets was right. When the comet of 1664 came he predicted its course. In his spare time he did many other things: he built a good many of the aqueducts that brought water to Bologna; he directed the works of fortification, and surveyed the waterways of the province. His fame went far and wide.

France was ruled at that time by the sun-king, Louis XIV, and Paris had to outshine all the cities of the world. The king founded the Paris Observatory of the Academy and, in 1669, borrowed Cassini from Bologna to direct it. Cassini never went back to Bologna. He was busy enough in the new observatory. There he discovered the inner rings and four satellites of Saturn, determined the exact motions of the moon, discovered the zodiacal light, the mysterious glow circling the heavens.

Measuring latitude. But all of this interests us primarily because it laid the foundation for the longitude measurements of the Academy. At that time measuring latitude was not very difficult. At night they measured the altitude of the Polar star over the horizon, and a correction was made for the distance of the celestial pole from the star, a little less than one degree (about twice the diameter of the moon, Figure 29).

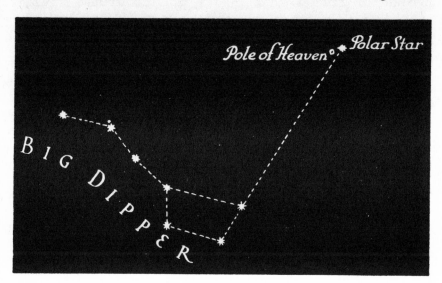

Fig. 29. How to find the polar star and the celestial pole

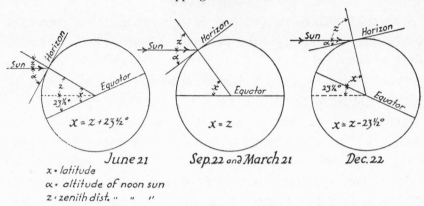

x · latitude
α · altitude of noon sun
z · zenith dist. "   "   "

Fig. 30. Latitude can be found if we observe the altitude of the noonday sun and consider at which point on our meridian the sun is exactly overhead

In the daytime the altitude of the noonday sun was measured. The celestial pole is the point where the elongated axis of the earth pierces the sky and around which all stars seem to revolve. On March 21 and September 22 the noon altitude of the sun would be the same as the co-latitude or zenith distance, Z (90° − latitude). On June 21, when the sun is overhead on the Tropic of Capricorn, the latitude is Z + 23½°; on December 22 it is Z − 23½°. For information about other days there is an astronomical almanac called an *ephemeris*, which has tables indicating that if the noon sun is so many degrees high on any particular day then the latitude is so much. Thus latitudes on old maps are fairly good.

Measuring longitude. But longitudes were another matter. There were no chronometers (clocks exact to seconds) at that time, nor any radio noon-signals to help.

Even at present the matter is not simple. The idea is to determine the local time by the sun or stars and compare it with the time of the prime meridian, or Greenwich time. For this we carry along a chronometer which shows G.C.T.—Greenwich Civil (mean) Time. For instance if our local time is 12 noon and the Greenwich time is 5 p.m., we must be $5 \times 15 = 75°$ west, as the noon moves westward $360 : 24 = 15°$ each hour. This would be simple enough if one day were as long as another. But because of the obliquity of the earth's axis, and because of the ellipticity of the earth's path around the sun, this is not so. For instance on November 2 the sun passes the meridian around 11.42 a.m., Local Mean Time, while on February 9, noon comes at

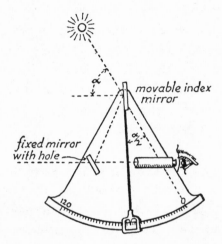

Fig. 31. A sextant is an ingenious instrument with which we can look at both the horizon and the sun at the same time in order to measure the sun's altitude on shipboard. (From Raisz: General Cartography)

12.13 p.m. It would not be practical for our clocks to show this variation so they show the mean time, one day exactly like the other. Thus to get the difference between Greenwich Mean Time and Local Mean Time we have to add or subtract to or from our local *sun* time an amount called the Equation of Time. This we get from tables.

Thus we determine first our local noon, when the sun passes the north–south line. The north–south line can be determined with the help of the polar star the previous night. Then with the Equation of Time we get the Local Mean Time, which we can compare with G.C.T. and get our longitude.

On shipboard the altitude of the sun is usually read with a sextant (see Figure 31) around 10 a.m. and 2 p.m., and with the help of tables and chronometers it is possible to get the local time, latitude, and longitude. The sextant is an instrument for measuring the altitude of the sun above the horizon on the moving ship.

All of this is complicated enough even at present when we have radio signals and exact chronometers. But good chronometers have been made only since the middle of the eighteenth century. Before that, differences in longitude could be determined only if the same event was observed in the sky at both places, such as an eclipse, the hiding of a star by the moon, etc. But for this one had to get in touch with a person living at a distant place, and a letter from Lima, Peru, to Paris might have taken a year or more for delivery.

Longitudes of the Academy. The French Academy, spurred on by Cassini, decided to do something about this. They made tables giving in advance the occultations of the four large moons of the planet Jupiter in Paris time. Then field parties were sent out to various distant parts of the earth to note in Local Mean Time when each of the moons disappeared behind the disk of the mother planet. Comparison of the local and Paris time gave the longitude. As the four moons of Jupiter

Fig. 32. The four bright moons of Jupiter frequently hide behind and emerge from the planet

58

revolve around at a fast pace and can be seen by small telescopes this method was practical.

Thus they measured thirty-nine localities. The results were put on a map drawn on the floor of a room in the Paris Observatory. This map of 1683 changed many ideas of where places were. It was copied many times and is one of the fundamental maps in history.

Fig. 33. Cassini's map has the North Pole in the center. It was based on the longitude measurements of the Academy

Jacques Cassini. Jean Dominique Cassini died in 1712 and was succeeded by his son, Jacques, 1678–1756. He was not so brilliant as his father, but he was a hard worker and a good observer. His chief interest was measuring the earth. His main work was the triangulation of France, in which he worked with his son, César François, and his cousin Maraldi.

Triangulation was not a new idea—it dated back to the ancients. To measure an angle exactly takes only a few minutes if one has a good

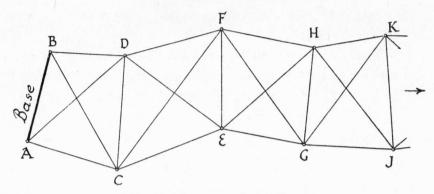

Fig. 34. The system of triangulation

instrument, but to measure distances exactly—even a few miles—takes days, and in wooded or built up areas it is often impossible. Thus the Cassinis selected a flat beach near Dunkirk and figured the exact location by the stars. Then they measured about five miles with the greatest accuracy. They used chain and rod, and measured back and forth several times, until they were satisfied. Then on one end of this line, at A (see Figure 34), they set up their instrument and sighted the distant towers of villages C and D, and measured the angles BAC and BAD exactly. Then they set up their instrument at B and measured the angle ABC and the angle ABD. Thus they had two new points fixed. They then set up at C, checked back on A, B, and D, and read the angles to E and F. Similarly, E, F, G, etc., were laid out without measuring more distances at all. Cassini carried the triangles south to Perpignan near the Mediterranean Sea, and there he measured a control base.

Ellipsoidal earth. This measurement gave him a chance to determine the size and shape of the earth, by comparing the position fixed by stars with the actually measured distance. Newton figured that the earth has to bulge out somewhat along the equator, due to centrifugal force, as a point on the equator spins around at about one thousand miles an hour, while the poles just turn in place. However, Cassini's measurement rather seemed to prove the opposite—that the earth bulges out at the poles. The question was hotly debated until it was proved that Newton was right, but the bulge is very small. The equatorial diameter is only a tenth of an inch larger on a three-foot globe than the polar diameter, something easily missed by the crude instruments of that time.

Triangulation of France. So the Cassinis, father and son, triangulated all through the kingdom of France, north–south and east–west, until in 1744 they published a map showing the exact shape of the kingdom. One of the odd results was that France turned out to be smaller than previously thought, and the king remarked that the Cassinis took off far more of his kingdom than all his wars were able to add. But he did not seem to resent it, as the Cassinis rose to high nobility and the son of Jacques signed himself César François Cassini, Comte de Thury.

Topographic maps. In 1744 and 1747 César accompanied the king on his campaign in Flanders and presented some detailed maps of that area. So impressed was the king that he then and there decided that the whole of France should thus be mapped.

The work was organized by César, and in 1750 the mapping actually began. But in 1756, when only sixteen sheets of the total of 173 were published, the work was suspended for lack of funds. César did not give up. He organized a private society to which the king presented all the equipment, and persuaded his courtiers to subscribe to the forthcoming maps. It took a great deal of persistence, hard work, and sacrifice, but when César François died in 1784 all but a few sheets had been published.

The first national survey. The *Carte Géométrique de la France* shows France on a scale of 1 : 86,400, an inch on the map representing about

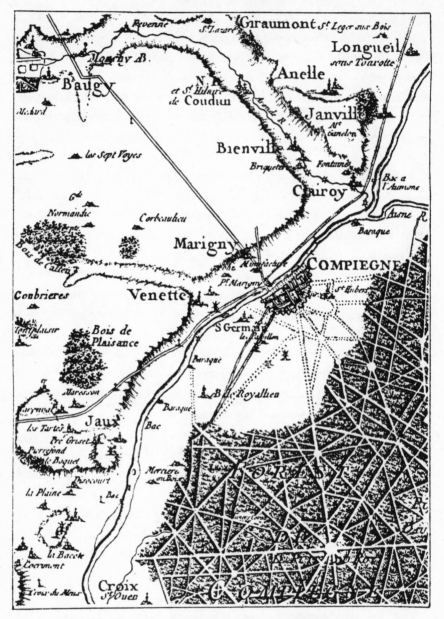

Fig. 35. *Cassini's map of France, 1756, 1: 86,400, formed the first great national survey*

1⅓ mile. If all maps are mounted together they make a 36-foot square. The *Carte Géométrique* is beautifully drawn—cities, castles, roads, and forest remind us of the charm of the French countryside. The lettering is fine, particularly if we consider that it had to be engraved in reverse into copper. Not quite so good is the method of showing mountains with a kind of rough hatching (shading). Yet the first great national survey and topographic set of maps will be an everlasting monument to the genius of the Cassini family.

Jacques Dominique. The set was completed by César's son and helper, Jacques Dominique (1748–1845), not without difficulty. In 1794 the revolutionists arrested him for his royalist sympathies and he spent seven months in jail. His head was too useful to be chopped off, and he was released. He was greatly honored by Napoleon, with whom he worked on the division of France into Departments and on the designing of the metric system, and he wrote a most interesting book about the four Cassinis.

With him the great line of earth-scientists came to a close. His son Alexander was a well-known botanist, not interested in measuring the earth.

Fig. 36. Inscription on the Cassini House in Paris: "Search for truth and follow the middle road"

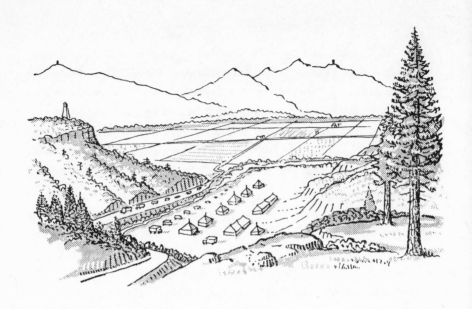

8

A TRIANGULATION PARTY

A long caravan of trucks, cars, and trailers was winding its way on the dusty roads of the Western range lands. It was a beautiful country of sagebrush-covered hills, rocky mountains, and grassy meadows. Gigantic pines grew in the higher valleys. The only people they met were a few shepherds and lumbermen.

The caravan came to a halt in a meadow, where an advance party was awaiting them, to direct each car and trailer to its prearranged location. In a short time a camp of about a hundred people was completely organized, and in a few hours the men, women, and children were able to sit down to their first meal in their new location.

This was not a new experience for them. They are members of a U.S. Coast and Geodetic Survey triangulation party, accustomed to living in different places every few weeks. The small community even had a large tent which served as the school, church, recreation hall, and

64

library. The children loved their camp life, as each new locality was a new experience for them. They learned first-hand about the rivers, mountains, trees, plants, and animals, and it was a sad time for them when they had to leave the camp to enter high school.

Selection of stations. The next morning the men set about their work. Their task was to carry a line of triangles (see Figure 34) between two points about 200 miles apart. The previous year a small party had looked over the territory both from the air and on the ground, and had selected certain hilltops ten to twenty-five miles apart for primary stations of triangulation. On their selection depended a great deal of the success of the survey. The places selected had to be visible to each other and with a good view upon the surrounding country. Some of the selected hilltops had roads on which trucks could be used, which was most welcome. More often they had to be satisfied with a trail for pack horses. And too often they had to carry the heavy equipment on their backs to rocky crags.

Near the camp there was a hill which fitted into the general scheme of triangles very well, but it was heavily forested. However, a road led to the top so they decided to put up a Bilby tower. Permission was obtained from the owner, and soon a party with a truck was busy on the location.

A Bilby tower. The Bilby tower is a light steel structure, which can be made 120 feet high to look over the trees. It is really a tower within a tower. The inner tower holds the instrument, and the outer tower has the platform for the observers and holds the roof with the lantern on top. The two towers do not touch each other, so that the people walking on the platform cannot jar the instrument. Both towers are triangular in ground plan.

Let us watch the building party in operation. First the foundations are dug for both towers, six holes in all. In these are placed the heavy base planks to hold the steel rods. They are most carefully underpinned so that the towers will be exactly vertical. From there on the work is a spectacular acrobatic feat.

Three men fasten the uprights with bolts, then they screw on the horizontals and the diagonals. For the next story they put a small wooden triangular platform in each of the three corners of the outer

Fig. 37. A Bilby tower consists of two separate towers,
one within the other

tower and climb up. One man underneath hands up the steel rods and the others bring the pieces from a truck. So they proceed from story to story, each six feet high, with amazing velocity. When they get up higher they fasten a pulley to the tower, they jack up the truck, and a winch attached to the wheel of the truck pulls up the pieces. In the incredibly short time of four or five hours the platform is ready over a hundred feet from the ground, and an hour later the roof with the lanterns will crown the tower. A concrete marker is placed in the ground in the centre of the tower for future reference.

Base measurement. As described in the previous chapter a triangulation begins with the measurement of a base line to establish a set of triangles. Let us leave our tower-builders for a while and see how our base-line party is coming along. Near the camp was one of those wide, perfectly flat, gravel-filled basins, so common in Western America. Through it went a road, perfectly straight for seven miles. There we see

Fig. 38. Base lines for triangulation are measured with extreme accuracy

men driving stakes on the side of the road. The stakes have a horizontal copper plate on top. There is one stake for each end of the 50-metre (about 160 feet) invar tape and one for the middle. Invar is an alloy of nickel and steel which expands and contracts very little with heat and cold.

The tape is pulled tight with a spring scale. One man pulls the tape, holding it over the stake, while the other makes a line on the copper plate when the spring scale shows a pull of exactly 15 kilograms or 33 pounds. On the other end two men keep the zero of the tape exactly over the previous mark. So they proceed for the entire seven miles, from stake to stake, with the most painstaking accuracy. Then they measure the whole length backward with another invar tape. If the discrepancy is more than one inch in five miles, the whole process has to be repeated. However, these men work so accurately that the average mistake is about one inch in fifteen miles.

Now we are back at the Bilby towers. Not only one tower is erected; this would be of little use for triangulation. Our group has eight towers standing. At present two are erected in front and two at the end are dismantled as soon as the observations are made, so they carry forward their sets of triangles. Not all stations are Bilby towers. On open crags a simple low wooden structure will do, which is mostly made from timber that can be found near by.

The observing party. It is a clear night. The observing party ascends the tower, fixes the theodolite, a powerful telescope with circles to read horizontal and vertical angles. They turn on the electric beacons and look around with binoculars. Soon they discover lights on other peaks, sometimes more than fifty miles away. They read the angles carefully to all visible towers. Microscopic graduations are observed and the calculations shouted to the recorder, a process which is carried on at great speed. But he can take them as rapidly as he gets them and can also make fast calculations to see that the two readings are very nearly a half circle apart, because if not the readings have to be repeated.

Why do they work at night? The main reason is that a pin-pointed light directed by a parabolic mirror, like that in a flashlight, can be seen much farther and more accurately than a tower by daylight. There is also less chance of reading the wrong tower as only those towers are lighted which are planned for the night. The air is also more quiet at night. The surveyor's bane is the sun-heated air which makes the distant objects "dance" in the telescope. One can also talk with the lights.

Suddenly a distant light signals dots and dashes. The men are experts in reading Morse code. They may tell you to take some extra readings to points where their own vision is fogged, or give instructions for the following day.

Not all readings are made at night. Besides the readings for main stations which have lights, a number of "intersection stations" are read, such as peaks, houses, towers, road crossings, etc. These are often marked with white paint or flags to make them more visible and to avoid mix-up. An angle reading from three or more stations will locate them on the map after the two main stations are placed.

As triangles are added, one after the other, errors accumulate—and after forty or a hundred triangles a control base has to be measured for checking. How soon this is done depends on the "strength of figure," which means the reliability of the survey. This depends on the terrain, shape of the triangles, instruments, weather, visibility, etc. If the control base differs more than one foot in four miles from what was computed by triangulation the survey has to be re-checked.

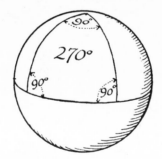

Fig. 39. The angles of a spherical triangle add up to more than 180°

Office work. The field work is only half the job. After it comes the work in the office. All triangles have to be adjusted. The sides of the triangles have to be calculated to correspond with the angles. The whole arc of triangles has to be fitted to the already existing arcs.

69

There is also another check. The three angles of a triangle on the plane add up to 180°, but the angles of every triangle on a sphere add up to more than 180° with the "spherical excess." The amount of spherical excess can be calculated for every triangle. For instance on the triangle in Figure 39 all three angles are right angles, adding up to 270°, the spherical excess being 90°. In triangulation if the measured angles are more than three seconds off what they should be the triangle is not used.

Laplace stations. There is one more adjustment to make which is somewhat more difficult. The earth is not a perfect sphere, not even

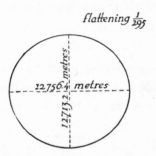

Fig. 40. In North America the parallels and meridians and the location of the triangulation stations are calculated on the Clarke spheroid of 1866

a perfect ellipsoid. But we cannot work with an irregular set of parallels and meridians; thus we use the next best regular shape. The parallels and meridians in the United States are calculated on the Clarke spheroid of 1866. This is an ellipsoidal solid slightly flattened at the poles and with dimensions as in Figure 40.

To calculate the triangles on a spheroid is difficult enough, but this is not all. We usually think of a plumb line as vertical and the surface of the sea as horizontal. The surveyor gets his horizontal direction from a well-centred level bubble (Figure 44). However, on account of the irregularity of the earth's shape, and because of mountains or heavier or lighter masses below, the horizontality of the level is not exactly the same as the Clarke spheroid at that point would indicate. This difference may make a much larger error than anything else in a survey. It is possible to check this, however, by making astronomical observations after about every twenty to thirty triangles. It would take us too deeply into astronomy to explain how this is done. The stations where these astronomical observations are made are called Laplace stations, and by comparing the astronomically obtained horizontal direction with what the level bubble shows, the "deviation of the vertical" can be figured and the necessary adjustments can be made.

After all the adjustments are made the survey has to be put into a form that surveyors and engineers can use. Each station has to be described, its latitude and longitude given, and the length and direction of each side of every triangle has to be recorded. For calculations the Survey uses metres, but for the public the data may also be obtained in feet. (1 metre = 3.280833 feet; 1 foot = 0.3048006 metres.)

History. The triangulation of the United States was begun in the first half of the nineteenth century in New England, along the Atlantic coast, and later in California. The first transcontinental arc was completed in 1878. Since that time the United States has been criss-crossed by arcs of triangles. Note the network of first-order triangles in a single state.

On every topographic sheet is found the note "North American Datum of 1927." What is the meaning of this? As we have seen before, every new arc of triangulation is adjusted to existing arcs or chains as we call them. As instruments and experience improve, the new arcs may be better than the old ones, yet they have to be distorted to fit the old network. Thus it was decided in 1927 to re-calculate the entire national network. Meade's Ranch in Kansas near the centre of the country remained the only fixed centre and everything was figured from there. Of course the discrepancy between the old and new location grew

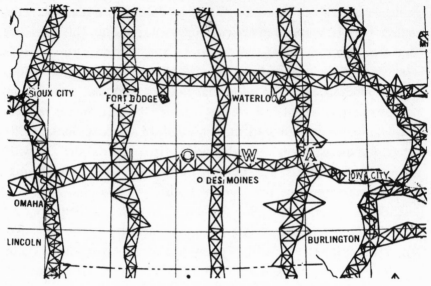

Fig. 41. First-order triangulation of Iowa

larger and larger toward the two oceans, but the difference was not much; around Seattle it amounted to about 120 feet. The North American Datum was adopted also by Canada and Mexico, so the whole continent had a unified network.

Topographic maps. To fill in the gaps between the large first-order arcs, the Survey makes second- and third-order triangulation until the network is so dense that there is a point fixed every two to five miles. Third- and fourth-order triangulation is often done by the United States Geological Survey or the State Surveys.

A network of fixed points is of no use if we do not make a map with them, and a regular set of topographic sheets is made by the United States Geological Survey. Most of the work is done by airplane photography, which we will discuss in Chapter X. In the past the work was done by plane table, a drawing-board set on a tripod. The plane table was set up on points of good view, and the plane table man sighted as many points as he could with an alidade. This is a rule with a telescope

72

attached. The direction of any point could be drawn with the rule and the distance could be obtained by sending out a man with a graduated rod. The more that could be seen of the rod between two cross hairs of the telescope the farther away the rodman was. The plane table is still a much-used tool for smaller surveys.

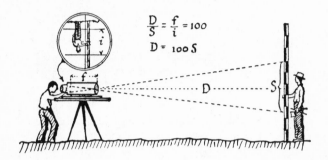

$$\frac{D}{S} = \frac{f}{i} = 100$$

$$D = 100\,S$$

Fig. 42. A telescopic alidade on a plane table will give not only the direction of a point but also its distance by the use of a graduated rod. Most alidades are made so that the distance should be equal to one hundred times the part of the rod visible between the cross hairs

(*From Raisz:* General Cartography)

State grids. There is one more service rendered by the Survey. Engineers and surveyors do not like to reckon with the earth's curvature. They like to figure with triangles in which the angles add up to 180°. The estates that they survey are so small that the earth's curvature is negligible. The Survey divided every state into parts less than 150 miles in any direction. They made maps of these parts in certain networks (Lambert Conformal Conic or Transverse Mercator, depending on shape) on which the scale-error is less than one inch in two miles, which is permissible. Upon these maps they drew a square grid which has no converging meridians and curving parallels as the latitude and longitude net has. Every point can be exactly located by knowing how many feet right and how many feet up it is from "the point of origin," an arbitrary point southwest from the state. This point is used rather than the central meridian and central parallel to avoid negative numbers.

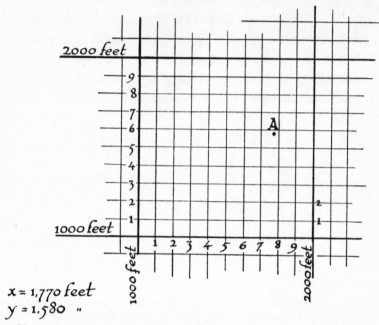

$x = 1,770$ feet
$y = 1,580$ "

Usually written as $A = 1.77 \cdot 1.58$

• Point of origin

Fig. 43. *A square-grid system*

The Survey re-calculated every triangulation station and the direction of every side of each triangle on these plane co-ordinates. These also may be obtained by request. Thus if anyone wants his property surveyed the local surveyor can find the next triangulation stations—usually within a few miles—and take a reading to them, and thus fit his own survey into the national network.

Levelling. When an engineer plans a road or wants to build a dam it is not enough to map the exact location of points. He has to know their exact elevation as well. It is true that the triangulation party measures the vertical angles also and calculates the height of stations. But there are many ups and downs between stations, and mistakes may accumulate on a long arc of triangles. For exact elevation, or as they call it "vertical control," the Survey has special levelling parties.

Levelling parties usually work completely independently of triangulation parties. They use different instruments and their progress is slower. While triangulation parties select the highest peaks for their stations, levelling parties like to go along roads, railways, or rivers.

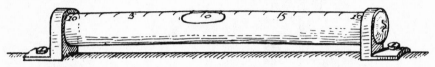

Fig. 44. Level bubble

Levelling is made possible by a level bubble attached to a telescope. The level bubble is a slightly curved glass tube filled almost full of a non-freezing liquid, like alcohol. If the level is horizontal, the air bubble is centred on the O line. Level bubbles are extremely sensitive and the slightest tilt uncentres the bubble. The level is attached to a telescope, which has a horizontal cross hair in the middle.

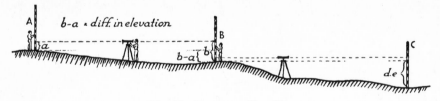

Fig. 45. Progress of levelling

The progress of levelling is simple. Let us say we level along a road. Rodman A drives a peg way down on the shoulder of the road and sets his graduated rod on it. Rodman B sets his rod down about 100 to 400 feet farther on the road, depending on slope. The instrument man sets up near the middle, makes his telescope horizontal, and reads rod A and then turns and reads rod B. Then he completely reverses the instrument and repeats the readings. This offsets errors in horizontality. Rodman A now sets up ahead of B at C and the instrument is set up in the new

75

middle, and so they proceed. Figure 45 shows how the difference in elevation is obtained. On steep slopes the rods have to be placed close enough to the horizontal telescope so it will not point below or above the rod. Readings are never made longer than 500 feet. Each line of levels is run forward and backward.

*Fig. 46. Levelling party. The parasol is not a luxury; sunlight
from one side may throw off the precision instrument*

The precision of levelling is amazing. They levelled across the continent and back, and came out with a difference of only a few feet. If the difference of forward and backward run is more than a quarter of an inch in a mile the levelling has to be repeated.

Levelling is younger than triangulation. The first transcontinental connection was made in 1907. At present, however, the network of levels is as thick as that of triangulation, as seen on the network of Iowa (Figure 47).

Sea level. Altitudes are reckoned from mean sea level. This sounds simple, but there are many considerations. When they levelled from

Washington to New York they found a foot difference in sea level. As tides in an estuary* pile upon each other, the level of harbours may be higher than the level of the open sea. Even if tide stations near the open ocean are used the surface of the Clarke spheroid is not exactly the same as the actual sea level. Thus they found that both the Atlantic

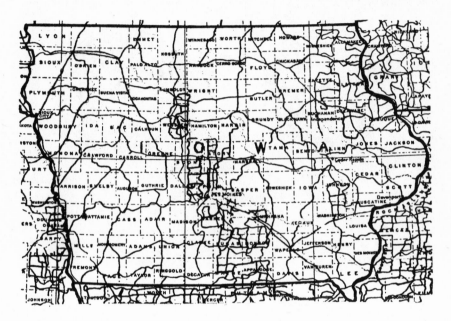

Fig. 47. First-order levelling net of Iowa. Besides the first-order arcs of levels there is a much closer network of second- and third-order levelling

and the Pacific coasts slope up northward and the Gulf coast slopes up westward, in reference to the Clarke spheroid. Furthermore, the Pacific Ocean seems to stand higher than the Atlantic. All these problems depend on the true shape of the earth and thus, what is a true horizontal surface.

* Estuaries are formed when the sea invades a river valley like the lower part of the Hudson River and of the Potomac River.

Bench Marks. Wandering along the countryside we often encounter bronze plaques set in walls, or ⊤ cut in rock or buildings. These are the triangulation stations and bench marks of levelling, and are the starting points for local surveyors. Respect them! To dig them out or take them as souvenirs causes infinite trouble and wastes a great deal of the taxpayers' money.

Fig. 48. Bench marks

9

CHARTING THE SEAS

Let us imagine we are at sea on a "tramp." A tramp is a kind of steamer which picks up cargo at one harbour and ships it to another, and does not keep very strictly to a regular timetable. These tramp steamers often pick up a few passengers, too, and it costs less to travel on them than on the regular passenger lines.

Let us suppose we sail the Mediterranean Sea and we want to get from Tripoli to Bengasi, the capital city of Libya. In Tripoli we picked up a cargo of dates, olives, camel hair, and wool; in Bengasi there will probably be nothing to pick up as the country back of Bengasi, called Cyrenaica, has not yet recovered from the war. We have, however, to deliver some bulldozers and steam derricks to improve the harbour, which was badly bombed during the war.

Next to the bridge on the steamer is the Chart Room, with drawers full of charts and also with books called *Sailing Directions*, *Light Lists*, and *Tide Tables*. If you ask the skipper he may let you see these charts and he may also tell you how to use them.

The ship's course. The skipper plans to sail along the coast guided by lighthouses until he reaches Cape Misurata, but from there he will cross the Gran Sirte (Gulf of Sidra) by compass in a straight line. Here one may say that there is no straight line on a globe, and this is right. In such a short distance, however, about 240 nautical miles, the skipper will not go far wrong if he uses the compass direction, although as we will see this is not the shortest line. His chart shows every compass direction (like east, west, northwest, etc.) as a straight line.

The skipper lays out Admiralty Chart 2158B which shows the eastern part of the Mediterranean Sea. Before setting the compass the skipper looks out for winds. It is one of those days in the late spring when the *ghibli*, the hot, dust-laden south wind from the Sahara, almost chokes a man. The skipper calls the Observatory and finds out that they expect to have the south wind for the next few days averaging twenty miles per hour. It would take the steamer about twenty hours to reach Bengasi. The wind would hit the steamer broadside and would deflect it northward about 4°, according to the captain's tables.

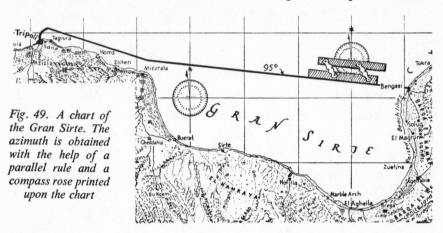

Fig. 49. A chart of the Gran Sirte. The azimuth is obtained with the help of a parallel rule and a compass rose printed upon the chart

If he sails in the true compass direction he would hit the Cyrenaician coast twenty miles north of Bengasi.

The skipper draws a line from off Cape Misurata to Bengasi. He looks at the line carefully for shoals or rocks. There are none present, so he lays his parallel ruler* over the line and moves it sideways over to the next compass rose printed on the chart (Figure 49). He carefully centres the parallel ruler on the compass rose and finds that the direction is 96° reading clockwise from true north. Magnetic north is 2° west of true north, so he has to add this to make it 98° magnetic. (What would his compass direction be if magnetic north were 5° east?) To this he adds wind deflection of 4°. Thus our skipper noses his ship 102° and sails into the night. He will check his position frequently by "shooting" the stars

* The parallel ruler (see top right of Figure 49) consists of two rules hitched together by two joints which can turn freely. The two arms are always parallel to each other. It is quite easy to make one from cardboard and the rings that are used in loose-leaf notebooks.

and the sun with a sextant (Figure 31), and also by the new miracle of navigation called Loran, described later in this chapter. He does not worry much about tides and currents as these are not strong in the Mediterranean Sea. Let us hope now that our skipper will arrive safely in Bengasi and deliver his bulldozers with good profit.

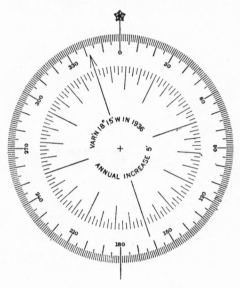

Fig. 50. The usual compass rose has degrees in the outer circle reckoned from true north and points (like north, N. by E., N.N.E., etc.) reckoned from magnetic north in the inner circle

Mercator projection. The chart which the skipper used is in the *Mercator projection*, a projection in which every compass direction is shown as a straight line. This projection has vertical, evenly spaced meridians and horizontal parallels placed at increasing intervals away from the equator. The length of the parallels and of the meridians have the same relationship on every small area of the chart that they have on a globe. The projection reminds us of but is not exactly the same as what we could get if we envelop the globe in a cylinder, project

81

the parallels and meridians from the centre and then cut open the cylinder along the side and lay it out flat.

Great circle routes. Now let us board another ship on the opposite side of the world. This steamer is sailing from San Francisco to Yokohama. Yokohama is almost west of San Francisco, and one may assume

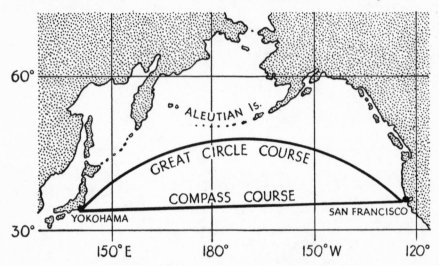

Fig. 51. Mercator chart of North Pacific. This chart will be used for compass navigation after the great circle route has been transferred here from a gnomonic chart (Fig. 52)

that the captain would set the bow of his ship to west and chase the setting sun. Instead, the captain will start out to the northwest and will sail west along the Aleutian Islands, then turn southwest along the Kurile Islands to reach Japan. Instead of crossing the ocean he passes along the northern borders of the Pacific Ocean. Why does he do this? The answer is that this route is shorter. The shortest line between two points is a *great circle*, a line cut out by a plane which would go through the earth's centre. Try to stretch a thin strip of paper between San Francisco and Yokohama on a globe, and you will see that the shortest line goes near the Aleutian Islands.

To lay out this great circle route the captain uses a *gnomonic* chart. The gnomonic projection comes from projecting the surface of a globe from its centre upon a tangent plane. It shows the earth somewhat distorted but has one great virtue: every great circle shows up as a straight line. The captain could not sail easily with a gnomonic chart because he has to use a compass. But he can lay out his course on it and

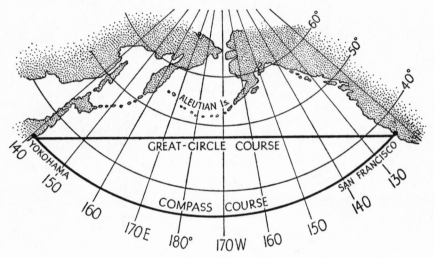

Fig. 52. Gnomonic chart of the North Pacific. On this chart every great circle appears as a straight line. It is used to lay out long sailing and flying routes

transfer it to a Mercator chart, as shown on the map. He has to change his compass direction every few hours but he will save thousands of gallons of engine fuel. Gnomonic charts for each ocean may be bought from the Hydrographic Department.

Special charts. There are many other types of charts. An interesting one used in America is the Monthly Pilot Chart, showing wind-roses,* currents, sailing routes, frequency of fog, storm tracts, compass

* Wind-roses are shown on Figure 53. The length of the arrows is proportionate to the time the wind blows from that general direction, and the number of barbs tells us how strong these winds are. The number in the centre records the percentage of calm days.

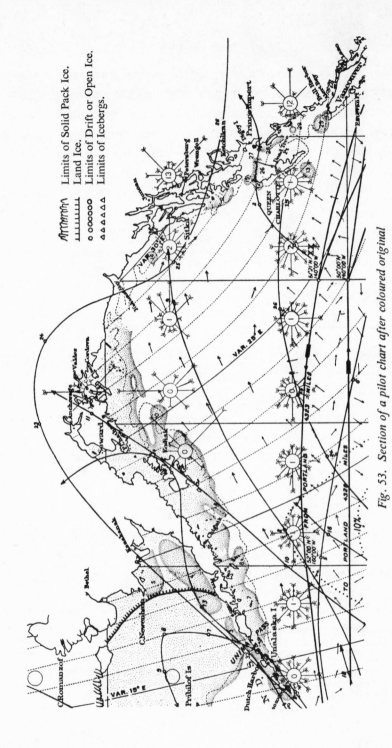

Fig. 53. Section of a pilot chart after coloured original

variations, limits of ice, dangers for navigation such as wrecks or icebergs, etc. On the back of the charts are articles on navigation and meteorology. Perhaps some of the most interesting are the Boat Charts originally issued during the War to help the survivors from sunken ships to find their way back to land. These show the rates and trends of all the main Ocean Currents, the prevailing winds, the areas of fog, the limits of pack ice and drifting bergs, the occurrence of heavy breakers, and the magnetic variation. On the backs of the charts are articles on meteorology, navigation and boat-handling.

Then there are all kinds of special charts showing earth magnetism, astronomy, radio aids, oceanography etc., which may be more interesting for the specialist than for us. But we may look with fascination at the charts showing sea-temperatures of the oceans. We may learn such things as this: the sea off the North Cape of Norway is usually no colder than it is off New York, nearly two thousand miles further south. Why? Because the Gulf Stream and the North Atlantic Current bathe the shores of N.W. Europe in the warm water from Florida and the West Indies. Otherwise even the seas round our own country would be ice-bound for long periods of the year.

From the Ice Chart of the Southern Hemisphere we may learn that icebergs sometimes drift up the coast of South America to between Montevideo and Rio-de-Janeiro, yet they never come anywhere near S. Africa or Australia which lie in the same latitudes. A chart showing the General Surface Current Circulation of the World will explain why: off S. America the bergs are carried northward by the Falkland Current which flows from Cape Horn to the Tropics, whereas in other parts of the Southern Ocean they drift constantly to the eastward, slowly melting in the process.

Loran. Previously, Loran (Long Range Navigation) was mentioned. This is a little more difficult to understand, but let us try. Let us assume stations A, B, and C give out short radio signals at exactly the same fraction of a second. If you receive the two signals from A and B at exactly the same time you must be somewhere on the line MN. If you receive the A signal in half of the time it takes for you to get the B signal, you must be somewhere on OP, because any point on OP is half as far to A as it is to B. (This line is a *hyperbola*.) So from the difference of time in receiving two radio spurts you can tell which line you are on. Now you watch the signals of A and C, and let us assume that it takes

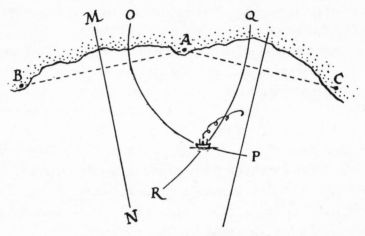

Fig. 54. The principle of Loran. The actual Loran charts have scores of hyperbolae in different colours for each pair of stations

two-thirds of the time to receive the A signal that it does to receive the C signal. Thus you must be somewhere on QR. The two lines cross at X, and there you are. In actual practice the method is a little more complex but the principle is the same. There are Loran stations every few hundred miles all over the world's coasts, and special charts are published showing a set of hyperbolae for each pair of stations in different colours. It takes only a few minutes to get the ship's location. For a short range navigational aid, the *Decca Navigator* provides similar position fixing. The coasts of the British Isles and N.W. Europe are covered by a series of "chains" which radiate hyperbolic lines in this same manner. Loran readings are obtained from a cathode ray tube and Decca readings from "deccometer" dials.

All seafaring nations issue charts. The British Admiralty provides a world wide series. As a result of resolutions passed at conferences of the International Hydrographic Bureau at Monaco, practically the same symbols are used on all charts which are understood by seamen of any nation. They help to bring the nations closer together. In the vast solitude of the sea, threatened by storm, rocks, and waves, one man is the brother of another regardless of the flags they sail under. This common brotherhood is reflected also in the international character of charts and the free exchange of information.

10

MAPPING FROM THE AIR

We hear the droning of a plane; we scan the skies, but only with excellent visibility can we discover a tiny speck slowly ploughing through the big blue yonder. The plane is a large four-engine bomber, but it is flying about four miles (20,000 feet) up. The plane is photographing the land below. This needs a steady plane so it may be kept evenly at the same level and not tilt with every gust of wind. It flies south in a straight line about 300 miles, then it makes a wide turn and flies back in another straight track to the north about twenty miles away. Then it turns again, back and forth, until time is up or the sky gets cloudy.

In the plane everybody is busy at his job. The pilot keeps the plane level at an even height, and watches his compass so that he will keep on the line. He keeps an eye out for landmarks, for it is most important to fly a straight line in the proper direction and at proper height. The radio man checks weather and flight information, and if he is tuned to Shoran* stations on the ground he checks the flight line too.

The navigator looks at the drag indicator, a vertical camera with a glass top on which a line parallel to the plane's axis is engraved. This will tell the "crab" how much a side wind will push the plane out of line. If the plane were headed directly toward the target, a side wind would blow it miles off the course. Therefore, the nose of the plane has to be turned somewhat into the wind. Airmen call this angle between the map course and the plane's axis "the crab." From time to time the navigator climbs to the small plexiglass dome and checks his position

---

* Using Shoran (Short Range Navigation) the plane gives out short-wave radio signals which are returned from two fixed stations. From the time it takes to return the signals the plane can tell its distance from the two stations. From these the plane's position can be triangulated.

with a bubble sextant.* His main task is to draw the flight line on a map, in correct position. The camera man is busy with his camera. He has already figured, from the speed of the plane and the altitude, how to set

OXYGEN

Fig. 55. Photo plane with single vertical camera mounted in gimbals

the automatic exposer so that the pictures will overlap each other sufficiently. He is ready to change rolls of film when all are exposed.

Trimetrogon photography. Maybe he is using a trimetrogon camera. This is really three cameras mounted so that one camera takes a picture straight downward while the two others take pictures obliquely left and right from horizon to horizon with a small overlap. Flying at 20,000 feet the vertical picture takes in about sixteen square miles, while the side pictures take in hundreds of square miles in the more distant parts. Only the nearer parts, however, are usually good enough for mapping, but peaks even a hundred miles away give useful checks. The centre pictures are taken with 60 per cent overlap. That means that they are taken at such short intervals that the next picture takes in more than half the ground taken in the previous one. Thus every point appears in

* The bubble sextant is a kind of modern sextant on which the natural horizon is replaced by a round level bubble.

two pictures at least. Obviously on the side pictures the overlap is much greater; distant features are seen on dozens of pictures. A clockwork is set to release the shutter at desired intervals and to wind the roll of film. The picture of a clock, a level bubble, the number of exposure and other data, etc., will also appear on each vertical photo. The whole camera is suspended in gimbals to avoid tilt, as shown in Figure 55.

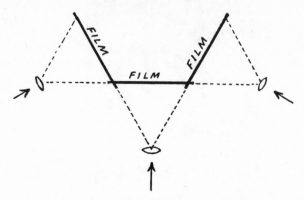

*Fig. 56. The three pictures of trimetrogon
cameras stretch from horizon to horizon*

Between 10 a.m. and 2 p.m. the plane had already made four 300-mile turns, on each of which a 25-mile wide useful strip was photographed. In a few hours it covered 30,000 square miles. It would have taken a plane-table party (as described in Chapter 9) several seasons to map this area at a great expense, yet with less detail.

When the cameraman returns to the laboratory the negatives are developed, cut, and printed and the pictures are ready for mapping. For the side pictures they use either a templet, as shown on Figure 57, or some prisms and lenses to transform them into maps. We will not now go into all the technical details of how the photographs are made into maps. This is a whole new science called *photogrammetry*. It is enough to say that almost all the nations are revising their detailed topographic maps with the help of airplane photographs.

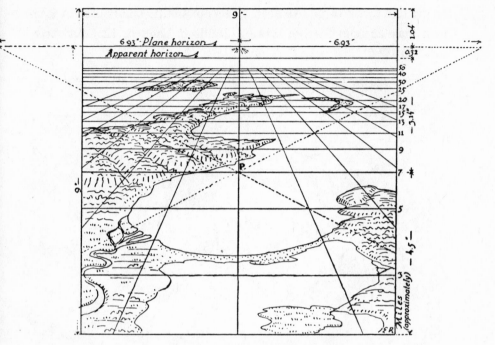

Fig. 57. Templet for oblique pictures

World Aeronautical Charts. The kind of trimetrogon photographs which we described before are used only for general maps showing large areas. The most important maps made with these pictures are the World Aeronautical Charts. These show almost the entire world in about 2,000 sheets, at the scale of 1:1,000,000 (sixteen miles to one inch). Important regions are at the scale of 1:500,000. This set of maps is used by pilots. The maps are criss-crossed by purple lines of radio "beams" along which the planes fly safely to their destination, over clouds and in the night. If a plane keeps "on the beam" the pilot hears a steady hum in his earphones; if he is "off the beam" he either hears an A (· —) or an N (— ·) signal. These charts serve the airman as the sea charts do the men on the ships. With them the flyer can safely cross the Sahara Desert

91

or the rain forest of the Amazon. Sheets of similar charts used in England may be bought from Edward Stanford Limited, 12 Long Acre, London, W.C.2.

Fig. 58. Landform maps give a better picture of the lay of the land than small-scale contour maps
(Wyoming from E. Raisz, *Landforms of U.S.* in Atwood's Phys. Prov. of N. Am., Ginn & Co., 1956)

Landform maps. The "trimet" photos are also used for "landform maps." These show mountains, plains, plateaus, hills, glaciers, etc., somewhat as they are seen from a high-flying plane. These maps are good to take along on the airplane and also on long car trips. They

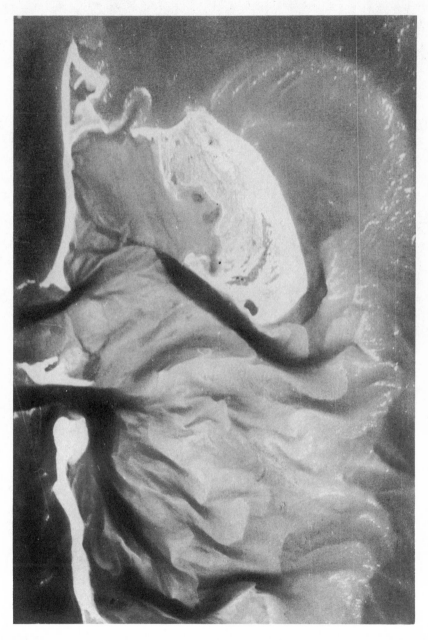

Fig. 59. *Submarine sand formations at Tuckernuck Island, Mass., caused mainly by shifting sand from tidal currents, known as "tidal scour"*

Fig. 60. Miami River, Ohio. Note dam, village, and farms with rectangular fields

help us to understand the country. If they are coloured to show field and forest, grass and desert, etc., they are called "land-type maps." These maps may represent a new direction in cartography.

Topographic maps. The most important use of airplane photos is for detailed topographic maps on which a mile is one or two inches or even longer. These maps have contour lines (lines of equal elevation above sea level) to show hills, mountains, and valleys. Pictures for these are taken from a lower height, and only verticals are used. The strips are so close together that the pictures overlap not only in the direction of flight but also sideways.

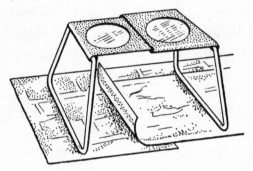

Fig. 61. A lens stereoscope is not difficult to make

Stereo contouring. The contour lines are drawn from stereoscopic pairs. Have you ever seen an old-fashioned stereoscope? Two cameras were set up a little distance apart, pointed at the same object, and a pair of pictures was taken. You look at them with a pair of glasses mounted so that the pictures fuse into one and the subject rises up so that you think you can touch it. If you take overlapping pictures miles up in the air, you can put them in a stereoscope and the mountains will rise and look as if they were real. It is easy to make a stereoscope from two lenses, as shown in Figure 61.

There are large, complex machines into which these overlapping

93

pictures can be placed and which will give this body-like image excellently. The machine has a floating needle which may be guided by hand around a mountain so that the needle appears always to be at the same elevation; if it is not on the surface two needles are seen. The motion of the needle is carried over to a pen which draws the contour lines. This method is much faster and more accurate than a plane table, but the machinery is very expensive. All mapping agencies use these stereo-contouring machines. The most popular one, the Multiplex, uses red and green pictures, and one looks at them with red and green glasses which bring out the relief well indeed.

Air-photo mapping. Airplane photography is the greatest advance in mapping in the world since the invention of the compass. The world's most inaccessible areas—swamps, deserts, forests, icy wastes—can now be photographed in hours, sitting comfortably in a plane. There are, however, some limitations.

We may draw rivers, roads, railways, fields, and forest from the photographs with the greatest accuracy, but we cannot name anything. The starting and finishing points of our flight have to be fixed by triangulation or star observation. Boundaries of towns, states, and countries show up poorly. Thus airplane mapping still needs a great deal of help from surveyors on the ground.

Airplane photos are used now for all kinds of mapping. The geologist can tell from them much about the earth's structures. The archaeologist can see the outlines of ancient cities where none were suspected. In England the remnants of a Roman legion camp were found clearly outlined in the wheatfields, to the complete surprise of the local farmers. Forest rangers can tell the amount and nature of timber. Crops can be estimated. Even the assessor of taxes uses air photos to figure out how much a property is worth. In this way, too, they found a number of hamlets which were not on any map and which never paid taxes.

In wartime, airplane photos are often the only means of mapping

Fig. 62. Lowell, Mass. Note the Merrimac River with its canals running into the textile mills

Fig. 63. New England landscape near Concord, Mass.
Note Concord River, ponds, hayfields, orchards, forest and sewage settling tanks

enemy positions. The U.S. Navy uses air photos to chart shoals, which show up excellently. They have found forms of huge submarine sand-waves completely unknown before (Figure 59).

Air-photo reading. The facing pages give you some idea of the face of the earth as seen from above. As we almost never see the land directly below us most of the features will look strange. They lack colour and even the tints are unnatural. For instance water is usually black on air photos. But if one analyses the size, shape, tone, and texture of the features and watches for shadows and approaches it is not difficult to read them. The best way to learn air-photo reading is to take a local photograph and identify the features on the actual spot. Nor is there a better way to learn geography in general.

11

A CONTINENT TAKES SHAPE

When Columbus passed a great expanse of muddy water at the mouth of the Orinoco River he knew that the stream which brought it was so large that it could not come from an island; it had to come from a continent. He thought this continent was Asia. Then came Hojeda with Amerigo Vespucci, Cabot, Cortereal, Cabral, etc., and gradually the continent took shape. After Magellan's voyage no one doubted that this was a new continent, and map makers got busy outlining it. The maps of La Cosa, Contarini, Waldseemüller, and Ribero in Chapter 5 show the earliest ideas of our continent.

Sixteenth century. The Verazzano map of 1529 shows a peculiar hourglass shape for North America. He had the idea that the Western Sea was quite close to the Carolinas. Fortunately for us he was wrong. Otherwise his map has very good outlines for its age. Note Tenochtitlan, the present Mexico City, set in the middle of a lake.

By 1580, the time of Ortelius (see Figure 25), we clearly recognize the outlines of North America as we know it today. But little was known about the interior. The Great Lakes, the Mississippi River, the Rocky Mountains were missing, and on many maps we see a great inland lake.

Seventeenth century. A hundred years passed. The Spanish settled Mexico and Florida. The French penetrated deeper into the St. Lawrence Valley and reached the Great Lakes. Between the French and Spanish colonies the English took a foothold. Figure 65 shows a map of the New World of about 1650.

This remarkable map was made by the great French cartographer, Nicolas Sanson. Have you heard of the Lost Atlantis? The old Greeks had a tale that beyond the Pillars of Hercules (Gibraltar) there was a

Fig. 64. Verrazzano map of 1529. The hour-glass shape of North America prevailed on maps in the second quarter of the sixteenth century

huge island, as big as Europe and Asia together. The people of Atlantis were defeated by the Athenians in very ancient times, and the great island sunk under the sea. When America was discovered, many people in Europe were convinced that this new land was none other than the Lost Atlantis re-emerged. The map in Figure 65 is titled Atlantis Insula, and the Atlantic Ocean is on both sides of the continent. Otherwise it is a perfectly creditable map of the Americas. It shows for the first time all the five Great Lakes and the mouth of the Mississippi River. One peculiar feature is that California is pictured as an island, although almost a century earlier Ortelius had shown it correctly as a peninsula. California remained an island on all maps until 1700, by which time Father Kino and others had reached the Pacific on foot.

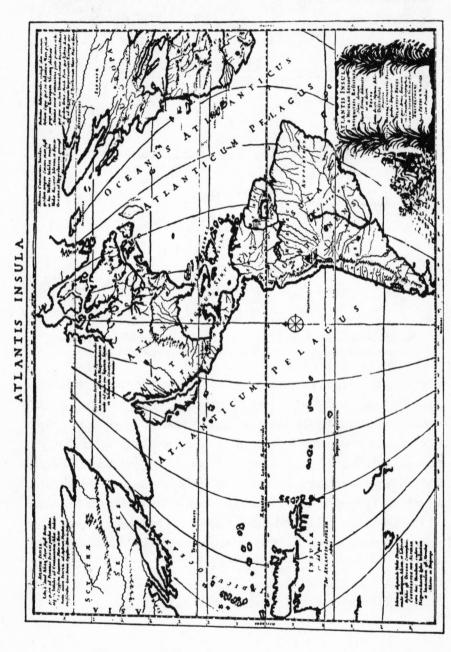

Fig. 65. Sanson's map of the lost island of Atlantis gives a good picture of seventeenth-century knowledge of America

Eighteenth century. Now let us skip another hundred years and look at Jonathan Carver's* idea of the shape of North America in the mid-eighteenth century. By that time the eastern half of the continent was fairly well known. The French had descended the Mississippi and

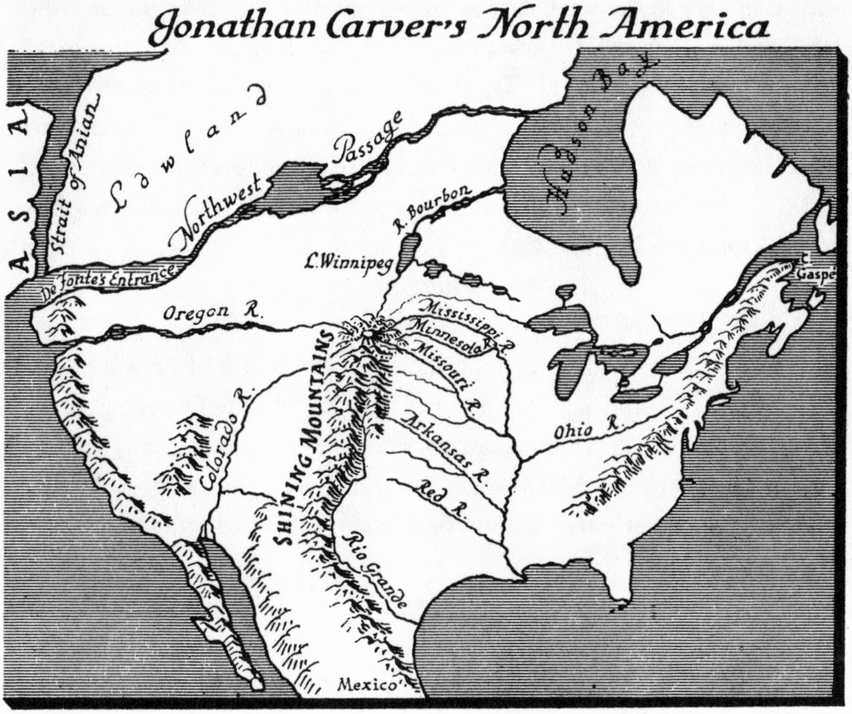

Fig. 66. The prevailing idea in the mid-eighteenth century was that North America was a sort of pyramid with all great rivers rising from the Shining Mountains in the center
(*From B. De Voto*, The Course of Empire, *Houghton Mifflin, 1952.*)

settled Illinois. The fur traders went each year into the wilderness of Manitoba and brought back tales from the Indians about snowy shining mountains in the west. The idea at that time was that North America was somewhat of a pyramid with the Shining Mountains in the

* Jonathan Carver (1710–80) was an explorer and map maker who traveled to Michigan, Wisconsin, and Minnesota. His maps and books are important sources of the early history of that region.

center. From this descended the great rivers. The mighty Mississippi, the Missouri, and the Minnesota Rivers had their headwaters close together. To the south the Rio Grande descended and to the north the maze of rivers of Canada. But the most remarkable was the Oregon River flowing to the west. As the story goes, this river was the invention of Captain Robert Rogers (famed for the Rogers' Rangers in the French and Indian War). To receive support for his explorations he needed a large river flowing to the west. The only such river known was the Wisconsin River. He found an old French map which was crudely lettered and the word "Wisconsin" appeared in French in two lines, spelled Ouisgonsint, like this:

Ouisgon-

sint.

The last syllable he did not read at all. In the first half he misread the "i" for an "r" and the "s" for an "e." So he got Ouregon. Carver dropped the "u" as an unnecessary Frenchism—and so, lengthened by imagination, appeared the Great Western River, the Oregon. Whether the story is true or not, it should be a lesson to all cartographers to letter their maps clearly.

This is not the only false story. Incredible as it may seem there are people who, upon returning from their travels, do not speak the exact truth but claim discoveries which they did not make. Even more incredible is that such people may become admirals. Look at the map (Figure 67) showing the discoveries of Admiral de Fonte, which appeared in 1752. This was long after the discovery of Alaska. What a pity that these wonderful inland seas and rivers between Hudson Bay and the Pacific do not exist!

Some decades later La Perouse and Vancouver came to the Northwest on ships, and Mackenzie crossed Canada by land; Hearne reached the Arctic Ocean without crossing the Great Waterway, and by the end of the eighteenth century the true shape of the continent emerged. In 1805 Lewis and Clark ascended to the headwaters of the Missouri and

Fig. 67. DeLisle-Buache phantasy shows the alleged discoveries of Admiral de Fonte

101

descended on the Columbia River system to the Pacific Ocean. David Thompson, working for British fur companies, perhaps surveyed more unknown land in the Columbia River Basin than any other man. Then came the fur traders and trappers; forts were built, and the British and Americans outdid each other in exploring the disputed "Oregon Country."

Nineteenth century. Yet the jokes in the mapping of the West were not yet over. Around 1810 a Mexican map maker, Pedro Walker, placed three mighty rivers on the map, flowing from the Rocky Mountains to the Pacific, right through the Nevada deserts: the Timpanogos, the S. Buenaventura, and the Los Mongos. These were eagerly copied by all map makers and the three legendary rivers did not come off the maps until the late 1830s when Bonneville's map recorded the vastness of the Great Basin. Nevada real estate would be worth many millions of dollars more if these wonderful rivers could be made real.

By the mid-nineteenth century the fur traders, trappers, travelers, geologists, botanists, etc., had left little to discover but plenty to map. The main difficulty was with the Indians. The fur traders made friends with them, sold them knives, guns, blankets, liquor, and trinkets. But the surveying parties came with transits,* rods, and chains. They did not want furs and it was very difficult for the Indians to understand what they were after. How would you feel if some strangers appeared on your land with weird instruments? No wonder that most of the early surveys in the interior of the continent were made by the army, or were protected by it.

Townships and sections. Almost all the land of the present United States, outside of the original colonies, was public land and the government wanted it to be settled. But first the land had to be laid out in

---

* Transit is the common name of a theodolite, the telescope which can be turned over on its horizontal axis.

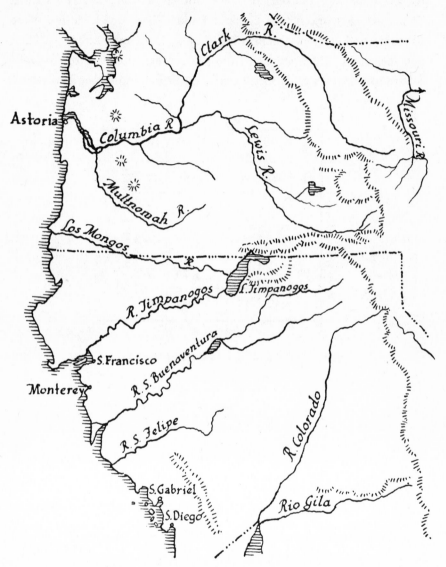

Fig. 68. H. S. Tanner's 1823 map of the West shows three legendary rivers

parcels; otherwise the settlers would not know where the limits were. This was the work of the General Land Office, which designed the township and section system. First they laid out the guiding parallels and meridians. Then, starting from the corners, they laid out six-mile square townships and divided each into thirty-six square-mile sections.

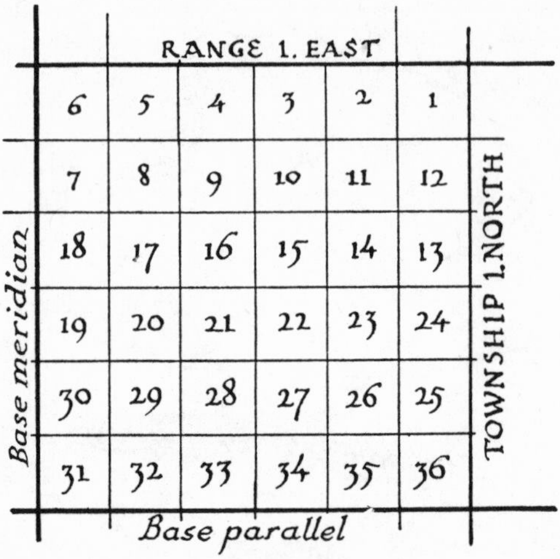

Fig. 69. The six-mile township and section system

The sixteenth section belonged to the school. It could be rented or sold, but the money went to erect a school. The surveyors of the General Land Office had to work fast because the settlers were waiting, not very patiently. The surveyors used the rod (16½ feet), chain (64 feet), and compass; they rarely had a decent transit. Sometimes, when later surveyed with good instruments, the townships looked like Figure 70.

But try to run a compass traverse* in mountains and dense forest! The compass is not a very exact instrument anyway, but often there is some iron in the ground which causes a false reading. One may check it at night with the polar star, but can we blame the surveyor who fell asleep after bushwacking all day?

* A traverse is a connected series of straight lines on the earth's surface, the lengths and azimuths of which are determined.

104

The township and section system had a great influence on the pattern of our country. It started the north–south and east–west pattern of our roads, streets, and houses. Compare the air photos from Ohio with the one from New England where the roads follow natural lines (Figures 60 and 63).

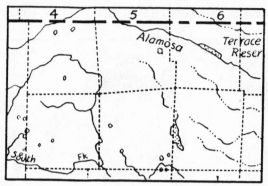

Fig. 70. Some townships in Colorado

The surveys. Even before the Mexican war many army and civil expeditions added their bit to the map of North America. In the fifties came the railway surveys. During the Civil War both sides clamored for better maps. In the seventies four parties were mapping our West. They were combined into the United States Geological Survey in 1878. We have already mentioned the first transcontinental arc of triangles carried through by the United States Coast and Geodetic Survey in the same year.

At present, with the help of airplane photos and modern instruments, the survey of the country is progressing rapidly. Yet it may come as a surprise that only one-third of the United States has good detailed maps. For another third older, smaller-scale maps are available, but for at least a third only medium-scale maps can be bought.

We have followed the progress of maps from the primitive maps of hunters and traders to the scientific maps of the ancient peoples, like

105

the Ptolemy map, showing the whole known world. We have seen how the invention of the compass made the exact portolan charts possible. Better sailing ships enabled the Spanish, Portuguese, and the other European seamen to discover distant shores and colonize whole continents. Then came the Age of Science. The earth was measured exactly, triangulation was introduced, and the first detailed topographic maps

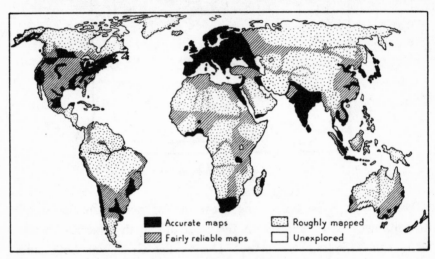

Accurate maps   Roughly mapped
Fairly reliable maps   Unexplored

Fig. 71. The present stage in mapping the world
(*From Raisz:* General Cartography)

appeared. During all these times the seas were charted with ever increasing accuracy. At the present time Shoran and Loran and echo-sounding help to chart the great oceans.

Figure 71 shows how far mapping has progressed all over the world. Air photos are available for perhaps one-third of the world's area, but these are not yet all translated into maps. The survey departments of most nations are working with speed and in a few years we may see marvelous progress.

We are now living in the Air Age. Since our ancestors found out how to make and use fire, and how to navigate a boat, and how to use a wheel, few inventions have come along quite as important as the air-plane. It is going to change our lives in peace and war even more than it has thus far. The forest of the Amazon Basin, the barren cliffs and ice of the polar regions, the unknown Sahara have had to give up their secrets to the aerial camera. As soon as a region is mapped it can be opened up with roads and airports, and trade and civilization will follow. Valleys have been discovered in New Guinea in which people live as they did in the Stone Age. Now they are eagerly learning the blessings and curses of civilization and it is our task to see that there should be more blessings and fewer curses.

The portrait of Mother Earth's face is not yet ready, but it begins to emerge in its full beauty.

BIBLIOGRAPHY

1. Bagrow, Leo: *Geschichte der Kartographie.* Safari, Berlin, 1951.

2. Birch, T. W.: *Maps, topographical and statistical.* Clarendon Press, Oxford, 1949.

3. Brown, Lloyd A.: *The Story of Maps.* Little, Brown & Co., Boston, 1949.

4. Greenhood, David: *Down to Earth.* Holiday House, New York, 1951.

5. Raisz, Erwin: *General Cartography.* McGraw-Hill Book Co., New York, 1948.

6. Robinson, A. H.: *Elements of Cartography.* John Wiley & Sons, New York, 1953.

7. U.S. Department of the Army: *Elements of Surveying.* T.M. 5–232, 1953.

8. U.S. Coast & Geodetic Survey: *Control Leveling.* Spec. Publ. No. 226, Washington, 1941.

9. U.S. Coast & Geodetic Survey: *Horizontal Control Data.* Spec. Publ. No. 227, Washington, 1941.

10. U.S. Geological Survey: *Topographic Instructions.* U.S.G.S. Bulletin 788.

INDEX

An asterisk following the page number denotes reference to illustration

111

113